ABBEY GROVE

Based on Jack Whitehall's
hit TV series

First published in Great Britain in 2013 by Coronet
An imprint of Hodder & Stoughton
An Hachette UK company

1

Copyright © Tiger Aspect Productions Ltd

A CIP catalogue record for this title is available from the British Library

ISBN 978 1 444 76301 0

Design by EnvyDesign Ltd

Printed and bound in England by Butler Tanner & Dennis Ltd

Hodder & Stoughton policy is to use papers that are natural, renewable and recyclable products and made from wood grown in sustainable forests. The logging and manufacturing processes are expected to conform to the environmental regulations of the country of origin.

Photographs supplied by Tiger Aspect and Shutterstock

Additional photographs: © Rex Features: 101, 105 (right),
© Corbis: 105 (left and middle) and © iStock: 99 (top right)

Hodder & Stoughton Ltd
338 Euston Road
London NW1 3BH

www.hodder.co.uk

Based on Jack Whitehall's hit TV series

BAD EDUCATION
Teachers' Handbook

Written by Freddy Syborn

CORONET

BAD EDUCATION 5

Miss L. Pickwell
Deputy Head Teacher

ABBEY GROVE SCHOOL

Ofsted
Piccadilly Gate
Store St
Manchester
M1 2WD

Dear Sir/Madam,

My name is Isobel Pickwell, and I have the misfortune of being Deputy Head of Abbey Grove school. Abbey Grove is at the bottom of a <u>nineteen</u>-school league table in West Hertfordshire. Unless, that is, you count St. Lucy's – little more than a cattle-pen for blind teenage arsonists with severe learning difficulties – in which case Abbey Grove becomes bottom of a <u>twenty</u>-school league table.

There is little that's intrinsically wrong with Abbey Grove. The school has <u>relatively</u> good facilities, very few broken windows and toilets that only fail us when the canteen serves its all-day breakfast. Granted, the gym has recently become something of a no-go zone, but that's only because the PE teacher's wife <u>finally</u> left him. There have been complaints, but (in my book) wandering hands turn a lesson into an admirable get-fit obstacle course. As I tell the girls in my class, 'If there's enough of you to get a hold of, you're not running hard enough.' I'd have got fat as butter were it not for all the many, <u>many</u> men who've been irresistibly attracted to me over the years.

No, Abbey Grove's problem is its staff. There are three <u>turds</u> in the watercooler: Mr. Fraser, Mr. Wickers and Miss Gulliver. This triumvirate has conspired to systematically destroy any sense of discipline, respect, competition and piety within the student body. Their crimes against humanity are practically numberless, but I have tried to briefly outline their major failings below. Forgive the diligence, but I am a child of the Cold War.

MR. WICKERS

NAME: Alfred Prufrock Wickers. Wickers' parents must have thought themselves very clever for referencing T.S. Eliot's Alfred Prufrock. Pats on the backs all round, Guardianistas. I share the suspicions Eliot felt about certain religious groups (suspicions I like to call 'scepti-Semitism'), but that does not make Wickers' name any less pathetic. Even worse is the fact that 'Wickers' is Alfred's mother's name. Alfred's father was born Martin Stool, but changed his whiffy surname upon marrying his now ex-wife.

AGE: Physically, 24. Mentally, 5, i.e. potty-trained in theory but, in practice, still apt to regress.

GENDER: Doubtful. Certainly, Wickers has a whelpish scrub of a beard. But I've seen many a bearded woman during my time as a knife-thrower's assistant in the Nuremberg Circus, and Wickers' total lack of testosterone makes me wonder if he's female. Either that or a eunuch.

MARITAL STATUS: In the Bible, when Abednimishackiah lies with every one of his fifty slave girls at the behest of Our Lord God, the act of sexual intercourse is referred to as 'knowledge'. 'And yea, Abednimishackiah knew each girl in turn,' it says in Isambard 2:54-56, 'knowing some on their backs, and some on top; knowing some fast, and some slow; knowing some from behind, and some by surprise.' Well, if sex is knowledge, then Wickers knows absolutely <u>nothing</u>. He makes the Virgin Mary look like a hussy. This is not for lack of trying. Rosie Gulliver has been the (what's the right word...?) victim of Wickers' ham-fisted passes for years.

CONFIDENTIAL

Sadly for him and joyously for the British gene pool, he's had no luck, bar one brief bout of tonguing at last year's school disco. I don't know what got into Rosie that night, apart from Fraser's spiked punch.

BACKGROUND: Wickers attended Middleton House, Hertfordshire's oldest public school. There, he was bullied for sporting inability, effeminate manner, pervasive odour and 'close' friendship with a certain Atticus Hoye, with whom things came to a head over an apple-bobbing bucket.

Mr. Wickers made such an impression at his *alma mater*, in fact, that his name has entered into the very language of that ancient seat of learning. To this day, when one braying bastard in a boater wishes to insult another privileged ponce, they call them a 'Wickers', to designate a weak, cowardly social outcast of absolutely no worth whatsoever.

To 'Wickers up something', meanwhile, signifies humiliating failure. So to say that 'you Wickersed up that high jump,' means that you've leapt backwards into the air, missing the crash mat and falling (painfully and with the grace of a leper) onto a boy in a wheelchair. As Mr. Wickers did at last term's sports day. Rem Dogg's parents were very unhappy.

SUBJECT TAUGHT: History, if you can call it 'teaching'. Mr. Wickers' classes are no more than half an hour's babysitting. In fact, I often think we should pay his pupils, because it must be a full-time job stopping an infant like Wickers from sticking a paw of wet fingers into a live socket or biting off his own tongue.

EXTRA-CURRICULAR ACTIVITIES: Mitchell Harper once told me that Wickers spends most of his time 'cranking'. I had no idea what 'cranking' was.

'You know,' Harper continued in that insufferably matey tone of his.

'Crasturbating. Giving himself a crand-job. Doing a Piers Morgan.'

By now I'd got the gist, but remained deeply unimpressed. Piers Morgan is an old flame of mine and I can categorically state that he only cries on nights when he can't get even the ghost of an erection going. We're talking no more than 60-70% of the time, as I told Harper.

POLITICAL PREFERENCE: He has no idea, as his father fills out his postal vote for him.

SINGLE GREATEST CRIME: I feel like Joe Poulter in a sweet shop: I just don't know which to choose! Not that I'm alone in marvelling at the catalogue of misdemeanours that Wickers has committed. For Stephen Carmichael, Wickers' dress sense is probably his greatest crime. For Chantelle Parsons, it's the fact that Wickers hasn't yet eloped with her to Bordeaux. For the police, it's the incident involving a Taser, a racist and a hall full of children. But I've thought through all of these, not to mention the many other nadirs in his autobiography, and after a lot of soul-searching have arrived at the conclusion that Wickers' single greatest crime is his ever having been born.

MR. FRASER

NAME: Shaquille Banter Fraser. Though I strongly suspect that 'Banter' is not his real middle name.

AGE: 36 allegedly. But that man is over 40 or I'm a Chinaman. And I am *not* a Chinaman. I respect their work rate, but modern China is far too democratic for my liking. Though I wish I could imitate its online policy by banning pupils from Googling 'Isobel Pickwell'. There's always some smart alec asking awkward questions about my youthful involvement in a certain 'ultra-Thatcherite' cell of lefty-bashers. Yes, I took a cudgel to a <u>female</u> vicar, but can't a girl dream?

GENDER: Male chimp.

MARITAL STATUS: The only ceremony a sane woman would enter into with Shaquille Fraser would be a shotgun wedding, and that is only because you'd <u>need</u> a shotgun to get her up the aisle. Maybe 'bazooka wedding' is more appropriate? Although that sounds like something I'd do with the girls in my convent back in East Kilbride.

BACKGROUND: Fraser's parents belonged to a great many <u>cults</u>. As a child, Shaquille (then known as 'Star-Banquet') used to follow them around the world as they took up residency in group after group of hollow-eyed, ponytailed, guitar-frigging oxygen-thieves, spouting pigswill about free love and Mother Nature. Fraser's cretinous parents finally saw sense and joined a proper church. This was run by a Christian evangelist who advised his followers to drink poisoned orange juice – once, that is, they'd changed their wills to leave all their worldly possessions to him. Fraser's parents dutifully drank the orange

juice, but didn't manage to die! What clowns.

By this time, Fraser had done what he styles as 'a Fray Prince of Bant-Air'. To those of us who don't speak Twat, he means he'd gone to live with his Uncle Phil and Aunt Vivian. This Uncle Phil and Aunt Vivian, though, were not a married couple, but one and the same person – Phil by day, Vivian by night. Which is obvious, really, when you consider the human trainwreck that is Abbey Grove's headmaster.

SUBJECT TAUGHT: Geography. This is just about within Mr. Fraser's capabilities, as Geography is just glorified colouring-in. The trickiest thing Fraser's ever done in a lesson is dislodge the green crayon that Joe Poulter managed to get lodged in his throat.

EXTRA-CURRICULAR ACTIVITIES: Inspired by the recent hip-hop-to-reggae transformation undergone by Snoop Dogg, Mr. Fraser has recently tried to reinvent himself as Fray Lion. This, he claims, is because he 'don't wanna push the rock no more, nah-nah pushing biatches neither, cos me getting in tune with the good vibrations, irie irie Jah.' As far as I can see, all 'Fray Lion' does to distinguish himself from the Imbecile Formerly Known As Fraser is to speak at half the speed while wearing an over-sized rainbow beanie.

POLITICAL PREFERENCE: If I had my way, I wouldn't let this man vote for *Britain's Got Talent*, let alone for a political party. Fraser has no real interest in elections. When he does remember to vote (which isn't often), he's guided by his habit of supporting the underdog. He loves a loser – hence his hiring of Wickers – and gives his vote to any small party he reckons 'needs a bit of a boost'. Unfortunately, this often means he votes for obscure and sociopathic cranks like the Green Party, rather than for the mighty UKIP, as I do.

SINGLE GREATEST CRIME: I'd have said the time Mr. Fraser had his hair corn rowed to intimidate the Middleton House football team was pretty loathsome, but Fray Lion really does feel like a new low.

CONFIDENTIAL

MISS. GULLIVER

NAME: Rosie Gulliver. Rosie. Not Rosemary, not Rosamund, not even Rosalina – Rosie's first name is its own abbreviation. This should tell you all you need to know about the woman's family. Awful people.

AGE: Rosie has recently hit the brick wall of her 30th birthday, a terrible moment for any woman. I'll be honest, I see a turn in her – if she doesn't start taking forkfuls from the seafood platter, I'll eat my trilby. However her dalliance with the softer sex pans out, though, I'm certain she'll return to solids. And I should know. I thought I'd be spared the almost obligatory biological-clock-inspired mental breakdown, but

even Isobel Pickwell briefly became broody. Turning 30 is to experience a Molotov cocktail of hormones being lit by time, then exploding into an intensely feminine experience which simply *cannot* be understood by men, as I explained to the officers who arrested me in the supermarket loos as I dyed the hair of a little chap I'd borrowed from his now-hysterical mother.

GENDER: Nauseatingly 'real woman'. Rosie recently tried to force me into discussing The Curse. 'I don't care what time of the month it is,' I told her. 'If you continue to address me in this intimate manner while loafing about the staffroom in pyjama bottoms, I'll burst that scalding hot-water bottle all down your front.' Gulliver replied with some pussy-parp about 'sisterly solidarity', but I couldn't answer back because I was too busy noisily choking back wave after wave of vomit.

MARITAL STATUS: Unmarried, and likely to remain so for as long as she flirts with officially becoming a member of Gulfie, Abbey Grove's 'celebrity couple'. Or at least, that's what Wickers calls it. He has also toyed with Wulliver, Ralfie and Gickers, but Gulfie has apparently stuck in the public's imagination. According to Wickers, Gulfie will one day rival Bennifer (Affleck-Lopez), Elvid (Elton-David), Rudy (Richard-Judy) and Giggs (Ryan-a female family member).

BACKGROUND: Rosie was raised by braless, be-beaded hippies, wallowing in their own gluten-free filth somewhere down in south Devon. From the stories I've heard of her youth, she was a rebellious teen, frequently seduced by the wrong sort: strong-headed gypsies, cricketers, artists, marijuana people, monks, union delegates and second cousins. All in all, it seems that 'cider with Rosie' meant less of an apple-based beverage and more of a handy-shandy. Basically, she got around.

SUBJECT TAUGHT: Biology. With such extensive experience of rolling about in meadows, fields, spinnies and ditches, it wasn't long before Rosie realized that Nature was her calling. Instead of becoming a fat-fingered farmer's wife, however,

she decided to go to Oxford. A big mistake, but at least it's better than Cambridge, where they're *really* liberal. I myself studied in Aberdeen (poly), and I still miss the tart sea winds, spittle-flecked church elders, granite law courts and horny roving dockers. Now *that* was an education.

EXTRA-CURRICULAR ACTIVITIES: Being 'nice'. Simpering bitch.

POLITICAL PREFERENCE: Oh God, she's as red as they come, this one. Rosie's just like most teachers today: all for the redistribution of wealth, but lay a finger on their precious pension and they'll bare their teeth like a pack of Trotskyite wolves coming down on a fold of taxpaying sheep.

SINGLE GREATEST CRIME: Saving Mr. Wickers from redundancy and/or arrest on numerous occasions. Those who aid and abet criminals become criminals themselves. When the (counter-)revolution comes, Miss Gulliver, you shall be lined up against the wall along with the rest of them.

CONFIDENTIAL

CONFIDENTIAL

So these are <u>monsters</u> with whom I share a staffroom. I wish my character assassinations could kill off more than their reputations! Miss Gulliver I would kill with <u>kindness</u> – kindness being the woman's most infuriating tendency. Perhaps I'd tickle her to death, or become her feeder, forcing her to consume so much Ben and Jerry's Phish Food that she grew to morbid proportions before suffering a massive heart attack. Mr. Fraser and Mr. Wickers would <u>not</u> be so lucky. I won't specify exactly what their fate would be. Let's just say that I've spayed better-hung dogs in my time.

Offing them has, I admit, become a regular daydream, one I usually entertain whilst wearing no more than a loose silk blouse, my heaving bosom pressed up against my father's dialysis machine.

Girlish flights of fancy aside, this dossier is merely the tip of the <u>iceberg</u>. But hopefully it will give you a flavour of the decadent establishment Messrs Wickers, Fraser and Gulliver run, not to mention the kind of feral beasts our pupils have become. And this iceberg – just like a real iceberg – will not melt naturally. As you are surely aware, global warming is the sexual fantasy of hemp-woven lesbians and their impotent, weak-wristed beard-men. I need you, Ofsted, to turn the heat on Abbey Grove.

Waste fuel, frack gas, chuck around Hummers like confetti and club all the seals necessary to reduce to slush this hateful, lunatic cabal before it's too late. I am not motivated by self-interest, but rather a deep compassion for the pupils I fear we are failing. Having said that, I'd probably overcome my naturally shy and retiring nature if you did want to put me in sole charge of the school.

Here is all the evidence you need. Burn this bastard down.

Yours,
Isabel Pickwell.

Class Wars

My most important teaching tool? The TV, obviously. My second-most important teaching tool? Jing. My third-most important teaching tool? Correct – it's my fancy-dress box. Because I think outside the box. What's in the box? Bullshit. (This is a different box to my fancy-dress box.) What's outside the box? Class Wars. (Having emptied the fancy-dress box. It's really very obvious.)

Class Wars. What are they? The sugar-coated differences between lords and parlourmaids in *Downton Abbey*? The savage cuts forced onto state schools by Old Etonian politicians? No. I'm talking about Class Wars, Alfie Wickers-style.

The theory is simples. History is boring. That's a fact, ladies and gentlemen, and it's easy to remember for anyone who's had to fight their way through a GCSE of Nazis, the English Civil War and [Insert random dull topic], let alone teach one. What conclusion do we draw from this? That facts are learnt through fighting.

'Clear the desks! Hand out the costumes! Jing, chain mail. Stephen, a crown. Joe, a massive hat with a sash, a buckle and a feather. (Joe's the hat guy because nothing else really fits him – big torso, tiny head, a bit like a Koopa Troopa.) Rem Dogg, here's a fake moustache. Mitchell, a fake wart. You'll see why you need it later. Chantelle, here's the fancy-dress box. Choose anything, just put some more clothes on and get out from under my desk. We don't study Ancient Greece and class wars does not include jelly wrestling on the Isle of Lesbos. So please wipe down my desk. It's really sticky. With jelly.' is what I said on that fateful day, except the bit about the Koopa Troopa. (Kids today know literally nothing about Super Mario. Pitiful.)

Let me paint you a picture . . .

It's a foggy June morning in 1645 (it's actually last Thursday) and we're in Naseby, wherever the hell that is (we're actually in the suburbs of Tring – its own battleground, as anyone can tell you who's had their microscooter nicked by Frank Grayson). The Roundheads versus the Cavaliers. A Puritan Parliament versus its autocratic wastrel of a king. Yeah! Now your blood's pumping!

On the Cavalier side, we have the foppish King Charles, played with dandyish gusto by Stephen Carmichael. He's assisted by his second-in-command, Prince Rupert of the Rhine, played by Chantelle Parsons. Originally Chantelle wanted to be in the New Model Army, thinking it was a Sky Living programme in the style of *Britain's Next Top Model*, only with an emphasis on boot camp. However, she's a very good aide-de-camp for Stephen, though I doubt Prince Rupert of the Rhine's skirt was tucked that high into his tights. If he wore tights. Though the name 'Prince Rupert of the Rhine' suggests that he definitely did wear tights some of the time. Maybe when his wife was out.

The Roundheads are led by Oliver Cromwell. Cromwell's played by Mitchell Harper (and his fake wart), because Cromwell came from

East Anglia and Mitchell's cousins were recently firebombed out of the Ipswich scrubland they'd parked their caravans in. With him is the ruthless Sir Thomas Fairfax, played by Rem Dogg because he'd brought a cosh into school that day and I had to cover for him with Pickwell by claiming it was a bit of Method acting.

(Maybe that was irresponsible, but I defend my pupils to the hilt. I'm the guy who swears to bouncers that those kids are eighteen. Sure, it's embarrassing being chucked out of Liquid in Basildon *again*, but I'd suffer any indignity for Form K.)

The King's army occupy a ridge along the back wall of the classroom, stretching from the villages of Little Oxenden to around the Babes Through History posters. Sir Thomas Fairfax, meanwhile, has been hoisted onto Naseby (my desk), from where he can shout instructions and cosh anyone who comes too close. Including me. Several times. I'm a victim to my art.

Hearing our merry lesson in progress, Frank Grayson and some of his chums knocked on the classroom door. He and I swapped some good-natured barbs, mostly to do with each other's mothers, before he asked if he and his pals could join in. Well, as we all know, in the Battle of Naseby, the Roundheads outnumbered the Cavaliers almost 2:1 (a grade probably only Jing is even aware of, let alone stands a chance of getting). So it made perfect sense to involve them in Class Wars. That's my excuse, anyway, and I'm sticking to it, however much you complain about my 'reckless dereliction of duty'.

Soon, Grayson (playing Colonel Edward Harley) and his hard-nosed Puritans are being faced down by the Cavalier cavalry, led by Sir

Marmaduke Langdale. Sir Marmaduke was being played by Joe Poulter, who was so nervous that the feather on his hat would not stop shaking. Wearing my customary black and white striped shirt, and with a whistle round my neck, I stood in between these rival armies.

'Cavaliers, ready! Roundheads, ready! Three, two, one,' I bellowed, in Scotch. Then I blew my whistle and unleashed Hell.

The first casualty is the Roundheads' infantry captain, Sir Philip Skippon, played with long-suffering loyalty by Jing Hua. Prince Rupert chucked his fluffy pink pencil case at Sir Philip, causing him to lose his rag with a stream of Chinese obscenities. But, true to his haughty Asiatic heritage, Sir Philip stayed on the field to marshal the counter-attack, which mostly involved lobbing chairs at the Cavaliers, King Charles squealing as one of them tore his pashmina snood.

Amazingly, Sir Marmaduke was having some luck against Grayson's Roundhead cavalry. This was because I'd persuaded Sir Marmaduke to take a play out of *Hook*'s book. To start with, Sir Marmaduke had tarried, asking what *Hook* even was, Alfie?

'You know, as in Rufio?' I told him.

'Who's Rufio?' the portly squire replied.

'Jesus, Joe, I've really failed you,' I said, saddened. '*Hook*'s only the last good film Stephen Spielberg made.' Sir Marmaduke made to argue, but there was no time to discuss the merits of *Tintin* (which, I'd like to put on record, is shit) because Colonel Edward Harley started raining down dictionaries onto our flanks.

Hiding behind a desk, I explained that *Hook* was about Robin Williams returning to Neverland to avenge the lost boys. Sir Marmaduke asked what Robin Williams had against Michael Jackson. I said Sir Marmaduke was being sour and dated. The point was, in *Hook* there's a big battle, and one of the lost boys – genuinely called Thud Butt – rolls down a gangplank into a load of pirates.

And so it was that Sir Marmaduke (Joe Poulter) rolled down the table at a forty-five-degree angle, straight into Grayson and his men. Sir Marmaduke may be a pedant, but he's also the bravest bastard I ever met. And whatever this kangaroo court decides today, I'm proud we stood shoulder to shoulder on that foggy day of June 1645.

But Oliver Cromwell wasn't having any of our 'Band of Brothers shit'. Cromwell hadn't bent over to aid Sir Philip, lest in doing so he expose his rear to the King, or words to that effect. Taking his confiscated paint bomb out of my naughty drawer, he lobbed it into the middle of the room and ducked for cover, as we all did.

When the carnage cleared, the first thing I saw was the outline of Sir Thomas Fairfax against the whiteboard, the paint having splattered all around him, stranded as he was up on Naseby.

For an eerie second, the sounds of battle died away. We soldiers swore we could hear birds sing. Then one man's wounded, heartfelt cry went up: 'My snood! My snood! My kingdom for a snood!' cried King Charles, shedding real tears but still acting his heart out. Stephen Carmichael: the consummate professional.

Then Colonel Edward Harley unleashed his own pyrotechnics. Smoke bombs erupted all around us, as more Roundhead soldiers streamed from Pickwell's RE class to do battle. By this juncture, I'd decided to become a Roundhead full-time, because I love an underdog. (Reckless dereliction of duty? Sorry. Think not.) The smoke added to the foggy-June-day look, though to be honest the whole thing felt more like the bit in *Platoon* when Charlie Sheen gets all Tiger Blood on that dick who killed Willem Dafoe.

Look, I make no bones about it. Shit got real. For one thing, I never knew that Prince Rupert of the Rhine used the Battle of Naseby to get off with a boy from Pickwell's class under my desk. But second base is second base – respect.

As I've told this disciplinary board before, I was fully aware I should call a time-out. I realised this just about the moment one kid was chucked through the window of my classroom. Thankfully, Sir Philip had opened said window to let some of the smoke out, otherwise we could have had a Cavalier musketman cut to ribbons all over the playground. But I couldn't stop the pupils fighting, you see, because my whistle had been yanked off my neck by Oliver Cromwell, who promised to shove it where the sun don't shine. I love it when kids get in character.

Then Pickwell herself burst in, looking for her class, and she swears I punched her. #winning. I'm joking. But as I've explained like a gajillion times, we were fighting over the religious and constitutional fabric of seventeenth-century England. Passions were high. Plus, Scotland was on the King's side, so she was technically an ally, making it no more than friendly fire, and who gets shit for friendly fire? America doesn't.

But you can't expect historical perspective from a woman who's slipped in a mush of paint and textbook. As she hauled herself out of the scrum, Pickwell began to get heated with me. Then Oliver Cromwell acted like a good WWE wrestling fan, using the chair on the truculent Scot. Again, I don't applaud this, but it was in the spirit of historical realism. And it bought me valuable time to play medic to little Anton Okwudo, who'd just been jabbed with a protractor.

Jing – realising too late that this was total war – had thrown herself over her work, but to no avail. It was ruined. I don't doubt she'd done something lame like cured a disease for biology homework, but Class Wars is Class Wars. There are no prisoners and no mercy. If Sir Philip Skippon couldn't take the heat, he should have stayed out of the kitchen. Then Sir Thomas Fairfax, dripping with paint, concussed me with his cosh.

The lesson ended with Mitchell putting to the sword the remaining Cavaliers: Sir Marmaduke, Prince Rupert, little Anton Okwudo and me. I remember being dragged across the paint-smeared wreckage of the classroom, past a small fire of Michael Morpurgos, before being held up against the ruined Babes Through History posters and made to suffer a full-frontal debagging. Then everything went black.

So, yes, five desks had been broken, numerous books were damaged beyond repair, and Sally-Anne Tibbs got a terrible rash from that paint. And, OK, the school nurse later ran out of Tubigrip. And, if you're gonna go *on* about it, little Anton Okwudo did break his arm. But who in Form K is ever likely to forget that the Parliamentarians captured the King's personal baggage, with correspondence showing his intention to seek support from the Irish Catholic Confederation through the Cessation Treaty? It's fifty-fifty.

That's what Class Wars is for. Come GCSE season, I just know my class's grades are going to skyrocket from Us to Ds. It's magic, bitches. You're not bitches, your honours. I rest my case.

Oh, PS: the school nurse found my whistle. Eventually.

> Having given his statement, Mr. Wickers sat down next to Mr Fraser, who 'fist-bumped' him. Mr. Wickers showed very little sign of remorse, though it would have been hard to make out his emotions from behind his two massive black eyes.

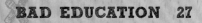

Graffiti in the toilets

Rem Dogg's mum does it for a tenner.

Mitchell's mum does it for chips.
Rem Dogg's mum is so grateful she pays you with chips.

Mitchell's mum gives you a palm reading when you're doin' her in her caravan.

Joe's dad retrained as a masseuse. Hannies all round!

Yeah, what a nonce.
Mitchell, wanna chuck firecrackers at Wickers after school?

Yeah, sweet.
Is this like your fifth shit today?

It's that popcorn chicken fam.

I know, bruv. I feel your pain.

Mate, next time, flush.
Ain't you meant to be usin' the disabled toilets, Mario Kart?

I would, but your mum's in there, givin' out hand-jobs.

Do one, meals on wheels.

Yeah, I am meals on wheels - every time
I done her, I give your mum a cookie.

oasis blur pulp

'OMG, this is so
#TimeTeam. Gaga
Rhianna Beyonce.'

Alfie Wickers = Pen 15
(does that mean I get to join the club, guys?)

What you doing in the kids' toilets, Savile?

You told me I had to write Alfie Wickers = Pen 1 . . .
oh, I see. You dicks.

Joe, you been eating pulled pork in here again? That shit's weird.

Wickers' mum is a swinger in Spain!

She is not a swinger, Rem Dogg. She has an alternative lifestyle.

Pickwells got a WANG

Sir man, what you doin
back in our toilets?

Pupils' Toilet

Staff Toilet

Aloha, bonjour and awooga. Fraser here.

Just to say, don't be alarmed by this. The PE teacher and Miss Mollinson have explained the whole situation to me. Basically, she was having a coughing fit and the PE teacher just happened to have an electric drill on him at the time. One thing led to another and – bang – there's a hole in my bucket, dear Liza, dear Liza. They both apologise if this hole gives you the willies.

Yours,
Fray Bantos Pie

WICKERS HAS WEBBED FEET.

Right, Pickwell, a couple of points:

1) Yes, I do have webbed feet. But is it my fault my family originated in Norfolk? Your family come from Mordor, but you don't see me going on about it.

2) Thanks to the webbing, my feet could hypothetically become very useful scooping devices in the event of both my hands being amputated.

3) If Waterworld, Deep Blue Sea or parts of Pirates of the Caribbean came true, who'd be laughing? Me, with my supernaturally enhanced flipper-feet.
Just don't expect me to save your
normal-toed ass from any mutant sharks/zombie pirates.

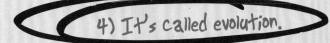
4) It's called evolution.

'THERE IS NO SUCH THING AS EVOLUTION, AND THAT IS A FACT. GENESIS, CHAPTER 1.'

5) You have a dick, so eat a plate of my balls. Boom!

I KNOW I HAVE A DICK, MR WICKERS, BECAUSE IT IS CURRENTLY VERY, VERY FAR UP YOUR A▬▬▬▬▬▬▬▬
▬▬▬▬▬▬▬▬▬▬

Please can you not write these things in a loo? It makes me incredibly uncomfortable. Yours, Rosie

Mr Fraser,

I have collected all of the hip-hop magazines you insist on leaving in this lavatory. You're not getting them back until you put creationism on the Biology syllabus, however much Miss Gulliver protests. Mr Wickers may crow about evolution, but he is a contradiction in terms. According to the 'PC brigade', we've advanced from apes, whereas Wickers appears to be going backwards, past apes, monkeys, orangutans and chimps. I wouldn't be surprised if he slipped back into the primeval swamp, there to devolve into a turd with gills.

Yours,
Isobel Pickwell

For watersports call
Mollinson, 07700 900817.

This is genuinely Mollinson's phone number! I checked. Her husband answered. He said Mollinson was all tied up at the moment, did I want to come round to watch? I put the phone down and had a long shower.

Was the shower golden?

No, Mollinson. Jesus!

Rosie, I am so sorry. I got drunk and drew this in permanent ink. I've been trying to scrub it off with white spirit. Please don0t be freaked out. And sorry about the smell. White spirit is really, really bad on a hangover.

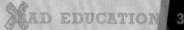

FRASER'S PLAYLIST

Walking on Broken Glass – Annie Lennox
★ ★ ★ ★ ★ 3.42
Play

Knock U Down – Kerri Hilton
★ ★ ★ ★ ★ 2.30
Play

Bump 'n' Grind – R. Kelly
★ ★ ★ ★ ★ 2.53
Play

Yellow – Coldplay
★ ★ ★ ★ ★ 4.12
Play

He's the Greatest Dancer – Sister Sledge
★ ★ ★ ★ ★ 4.26
Play

Bring Him Home – Les Miserables
★ ★ ★ ★ ★ 4.58
Play

Murder She Wrote – Chaka Demus and Pliers
★ ★ ★ ★ ★ 3.57
Play

Addicted To Love – Tina Turner
★ ★ ★ ★ ★ 3.12
Play

Dancing With Myself –Billy Idol
★ ★ ★ ★ ★ 4.02
Play

One Way or Another – One Direction
★ ★ ★ ★ ★ 3.40
Play

Walking on Broken Glass – Annie Lennox
★ ★ ★ ★ ★ 3.42
Play

Walking on Broken Glass – Annie Lennox
★ ★ ★ ★ ★ 3.42
Play

Fraser's Perfect Party Playlist

Want some fat tunes but don't have the time to develop a flawless taste in music? Then look no further. This playlist is perfect for weddings, sweet sixteenths, wakes (proof: my mother's wake went with a swing), baptisms and leaving parties, unless you've made the person leaving redundant yourself.

It's not ideal for bar mitzvahs. Particularly during the chanty bits.

1. Walking on Broken Glass – Annie Lennox

I love Annie Lennox so much that I actually used to think I was gay. This was due to a slight mix-up *vis-à-vis* who was who in the Eurhythmics. In my head, Dave Stewart was Annie and Annie was Dave. I'm not slighting Annie's looks. Quite the opposite, in fact. But bear in mind I'd popped de ole cherry on the belly of a woman who looked just like Dave Stewart. She had a heart of gold, but also a beard of gold, flecked with grey.

By the end of the 1980s I was bewitched by 'Dave'. So I decided to tell my parents that grandkids weren't really on the cards. And remember that this was way before Elton and David Furnish, or He Who Must Not Be Named. Not Voldemort – you know, the movie star in the closet. Short hair. He's in *Vanilla Sky*, *Minority Report* and *Knight and Day*. Man's name starting with a C? Goofy face? Blonde? Tall? It's Cameron bloody Diaz! The guy went out with Justin Timberlake for like three years. Talk about hiding in plain sight.

Anyway, I expected to be 'walking on broken glass' with my parents. They're very religious people – having belonged to a number of different cults over the years – and I thought my sexuality would cause big trouble.

'Mum, Dad, can you stop hopping around Oxford St in orange robes for a second? That's right, put the tambourine down,' I said. 'Here's the weather with Shaquille Fraser. Outlook: light showers, causing me to squeal, put my waistcoat over my immaculate hair and dash under the awning of a *boulangerie*, jumping some puddles so I don't get my light suede penny loafers wet. My parents didn't seem to get the message. Dad even started fiddling with the tambourine again.'

'Mum, Dad, I'm gay,' I said. It was a weight off my shoulders. I felt giddy from the relief and – yes – the pride. I am what I am. Or, rather, was what I thought I was. And, whatever they felt in private, I'll give my mum and dad this: they certainly didn't *seem* surprised.

It only started to dawn on me that I might actually be heterosexual at uni. Lowestoft is a cosmopolitan place, you see, so it wasn't long before I'd hooked up with a chap called Roland. He had a perm as voluminous as Brian May's, which suited me because I was also crazy about Queen! I wasn't so crazy about Roland's Freddie Mercury moustache/stubble combo, but you can't have all your eggs up Shit Creek. I mean, your grandmother sucks bears in the woods, right?

But then, in that long, hot summer of '92, *Walking on Broken Glass* came out and I went 'back in'.

I can remember Roland playing the song to me on a single he'd bought that day. The sound washed over me like liquid sunlight. 'My God,' I cried, 'who's singing this beautiful music?' When Roland showed me the single sleeve, my whole world imploded. There was Dave Stewart – and under 'him', the words *Annie Lennox*!

Thus ended my period of sexual confusion. All in all, I'd had fun as a gay man. I'd got to dress well, learn how to cook and go shirtless indoors. But Annie Lennox was the final piece of the puzzle, and the puzzle

now looked liked Shaquille Fraser. So I bade Roland a tearful farewell, put on my shirt and left Lowestoft before technically receiving any qualifications whatsoever. In the words of Justin Lee Collins (who, come to think about it, also reminds me of the lady I lost my virginity to), 'good times'.

2. Bump 'n' Grind – R. Kelly

Quite simply, this is *the* track to show off your moves. 'My mind's telling me no, but my body, my body's telling me yes!' R. Kelly sings. I know exactly what he means. My summer of love with Roland was basically exactly the same, only my mind was telling me yes, but my body, my body was telling me 'Hang on a tick...'

Note: maybe skip this track at wakes. It has an odd effect on mourners, however drunk they are at the time.

3. He's The Greatest Dancer – Sister Sledge

He's The Greatest Dancer – a phrase yours truly has heard said about him countless times (twice). And once you get dutty to *Bump 'n' Grind*, you'll feel the Sister's affirmation is nothing more than the compliment you deserve, too.

4. Murder She Wrote – Chaka Demus and Pliers

The definitive reggae-reggae sauce, written by the Lennon and McCartney of 90s dancehall-pop crossover anthems. *Murder, She Wrote* is also my favourite TV show, reminding me of the many happy months I've spent being unemployed.

I recently wrote to Chaka Demus and Pliers on that topic, in my new guise as Fray Lion. *Hail the selector!* In my letter, I suggested a whole album of daytime-TV-inspired reggae hits. One was called *Silver Fatherman*, to celebrate Philip Schofield. Another was called *Loose Clart* (chorus: 'Bellingham, McClean and Welch got me sweatin' | me heart poundin', me stiffin' for McGiffin | hail him, hail him'.) I also came up with a line that went 'Me gonna send him to outer space | to find another bargain,' but I'm the first to admit I never cracked the *Bargain Hunt* motif.

My favourite suggestion, though, was a stone-cold hit: *Jah Make Me Kyle-ie*. Yessim, this is a song about that warm, eerie glow you get when watching ex-gambling addict Jeremy Kyle shoving another under-privileged manic depressive into a sack of past misdemeanours, weighing them down with some rocks of DNA evidence, then booting it off the truth-cliff into a sea of ruined lives. What's that? Your brain's numb, you can't think and there's an acrid, burning taste in the back of your mouth. You *must* be 'Kyle-ie'! And getting Kyle-ie gives you the munchies *baaadd*. I mean, I heard they had to install extra-wide metal detectors for his studio audience.

In a cruel twist of fate, however, I imagine Chaka Demus and Pliers were both too busy watching these shows to reply, because I haven't heard *anything* by them for years. Typical of the unemployed. Won't help themselves. That's what Kyle says. Anyway, their niche is long gone since his Imperial Majesty Olly Murs re-invented reggae.

5. Dancing With Myself – Billy Idol

Idol is the ultimate dancer: he talks with his pelvis. He also wears netted waistcoats, which are my guilty pleasure on a night out. Plus, the dystopian, tramp-filled city in the music video reminds me of Lowestoft.

Admittedly, the tramps in Lowestoft did less dancing and more goodness-knows-whatting in their trousers, but you get my drift.

And talking of guilty – guilty, guilty, guilty as a girl can be (to quote Bananarama!) – I also dance by myself a lot. At home, in the office, in discos etc. Some people say this is depressing, but I like to think of it as a bit of me-time for The Greatest Dancer©.

6. Walking on Broken Glass – Annie Lennox

It's the best song in the world. Go on, play it twice.

7. Knock U Down – Keri Hilton

I include this mostly for Ne-Yo's flow about being 'commander-in-chief of my pimp ship,' the best single lyric ever written, and one that so neatly mirrors my own life. After all, I've often thought I'm the new Slick Rick. Ask me anything about teenage love – I see a new position every time I go to the bike shed to collect my tricycle.

And Abbey Grove's board of governors may have officially forbidden me from changing my title from 'headmaster' to 'commander-in-chief', and Abbey Grove's name to

'Pimp Ship', but so what? I'm flying, we ain't crashing, and no pretty little miss (in the guise of Ofsted) is gonna shoot us out the sky.

8. Yellow – *Coldplay*

What can you say? They're tunesmiths, they fill arenas and they look like Geography teachers (khaki's not coming back in *because it never went away*). All in all, Coldplay provide the perfect soundtrack to my geography classes. And, because Geography is just colouring in, and 'Yellow' is such a bloomin' catchy song, I tend to teach the yellow things in the world, like the Yellow River, deserts, and the Canary Islands.

My dirty little secret, though, is that I privately don't like the colour yellow. So when I'm singing along to this by myself, I substitute the word 'yellow' for either 'mellow' (because it usually is, aaaaiiiii), 'red' (my favourite colour) or 'Pellow' if it's raining, because I think it's a clever link back to Wet, Wet, Wet via their charismatic front man Marti Pellow. Interestingly, I once met Marti when he was on tour with his prodution of *Jekyll and Hyde*. I was hanging around backstage holding a mop. It's ludicrously easy to be admitted to mediocre regional theatres like this; I met Lee Meade in Andover, Lenny Henry in Doncaster and June Whitfield in Ipswich, Preston, Buxton, Canterbury and Crewe, before 'her people' warned me off the Southampton gig.

Anyway, I sang *Yellow* to Pellow, using 'Pellow' instead of 'yellow'. I couldn't say for sure how Marti felt about it – his features were still hidden behind Mr. Hyde's sideburns and snout – but the police were very courteous.

9. Bring Him Home – *Les Miserables*

I've wept openly every one of the 37 times I've seen the stage show of *Les Mis* in London. The show's hero, Jean Valjean, is more than a man. He is a way of life. That's why I'm so kind to Alfie Wickers, who's a lost little boy in the mould of Marius. In fact, I've often told Alfie he looks just like a fat Eddie Redmayne. He doesn't like that. But however rude he is back to me, I'm still his Valjean. I'm going to make sure he survives the war, and if that means dragging him through the overflowing sewers of nineteenth-century Paris, then so be it. My Crocs sponge down a treat.

I would only hold this selfless heroism against Alfie if he subsequently goes to seed in the style of the original Marius, Michael Ball. That guy really needs to take a look at himself in the mirror. Ball was the definitive Marius, for God's sake, but could even Jean Valjean drag him through a sewer nowadays? I sincerely doubt it. Michael Ball *disgusts* me.

Back to the playlist. Granted, *Bring Him Home* isn't very dancey, but just listen to those high notes. Impossible for all but the best singers, amongst whose company I count Alfie Boe, myself and Billy Idol.

Note: this one is really good for wakes, so maybe substitute it for *Bump 'n' Grind* and slap on *Mr. Mistoffelees* from *Cats* at number 8.

(*Cats* is amazing, but other stuff by T.S. Eliot is very, very weak. Half of it doesn't even rhyme. Eliot: less conjuring cat, more rob-dog.)

10. Addicted To Love – Tina Turner

Great tune. Why? Because it was made in a time when – by law – saxophonists could only wear sleeveless leather jackets. People who don't love this song don't love. Full stop.

I've only been addicted to love once. The lady in question was older than me, so she knew the ropes, and by God I couldn't quit her! I needed hit after hit of her sweet brown sugar, pumped straight into my bulging, waxen veins. Sometimes, I'd end up stealing because I couldn't afford to take her to dinner that night. She loved dinner. Did I mention she was a big lady? She had an Evans loyalty card and, no, I mean a card for Evans outsized, not for Evans bicycles. (I imagine it's pretty rare to find someone with both.)

Then, one night, she promised to take *me* to dinner, her treat. Well, Dutch, but it was something – for the sake of her appetite, I'd already pawned my Nissan Cherry, my VHS player and all my parents' cult paraphernalia (this was post-orange juice, so they were none the wiser). Anyway, she wanted to take me to a hip, exclusive new Asian restaurant in town. She said she needed my credit card to book our table. And my drivers' licence. And my national insurance number. And all my passwords. But when I arrived at Wagamamas, she was nowhere to be seen. That was some cold turkey, I can tell you. I couldn't get out of bed for weeks, not even to beg with the bailiffs.

11. One Way Or Another — *One Direction*

Yes, there are purists (snobs) who say that Blondie's *One Way Or Another* is better. But what could be more endearing than five poontang-crazy men cooing the lyrics 'one way or another I'm gonna getcha, I'm gonna getcha, getcha, getcha, getcha' at the tweenage girls who make up 99.999% of their audience? (The other 0.001%? Moi.)

Harry Styles. I have *never* wanted to be someone more than that debonair little bugger. Genuinely, if I had to choose between being H. Sty or my previous no.1, Hunter from *Gladiator*, I'd be getting yet another comically bad tattoo drawn on my boy's torso like a flash. Plus, I'd get to sleep with Caroline Flack.

Also, Debbie Harry is just a poor man's Annie Lennox. 1D's Niall, on the other hand... let's just say, if I was still the impressionable young dude I was in '92, I'd probably think Niall was a boy too! How she deals with the four lads on a night out I'll never know! Hats off to her, I say. It can't be easy, being a lady and looking so much like that bloke Cameron Diaz.

12. Walking On Broken Glass — *Annie Lennox*

Because she is the beginning, middle and end of me. If people really hated the second time you played it, maybe swap it for *Little Bird*.

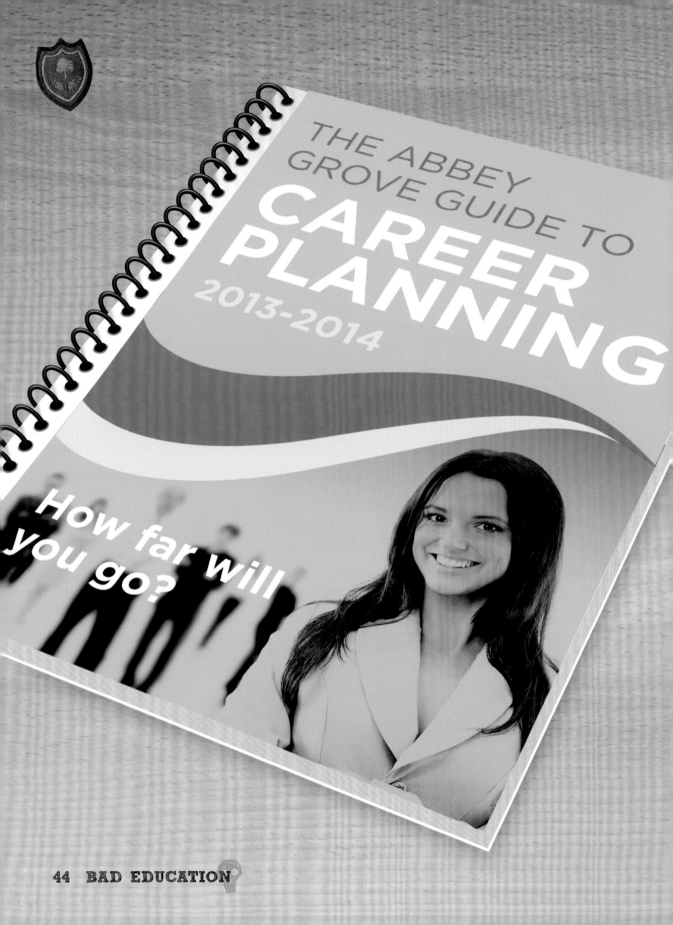

THE ABBEY GROVE GUIDE TO
CAREER PLANNING
2013-2014

How far will you go?

Foreword by Miss Gulliver

Hi everyone,

Attached is a careers questionnaire we've been asked to get you to fill in. It's been written by UCAS, the university placement service that you'll hopefully be using in a few years' time. And I think it's really important that you all start thinking seriously about what you'd like to do with your lives, because this will affect your choices of AS/A2 levels.

I remember when I first realised I wanted to become a teacher. In the summer of my GCSEs, my girls' school hired a new English teacher. Mr. Ellis taught us Byron by taking us for long walks in the woods, reciting poetry by heart as we communed with nature. And it was amongst those trees – my bare feet dancing over the hot earth and cool, ripe grass, my body on the cusp of womanhood – that I fell in love with him.

In the early summer sun of 1997, Simon Ellis looked almost impossibly Romantic: a strong jaw, broad chest and wave upon wave of dark, curly hair. But his eyes! His eyes were the most extraordinary things I'd ever seen. When he quoted Byron, they flashed with a feeling strong enough to destroy worlds. I can still quote the passage from *Don Juan* that made my knees weak one hot May morning, so closely did it chime with the blind devotion I felt for Mr. Ellis then:

> 'I loved, I love you, for that love have lost
>   State, station, heaven, mankind's, my own esteem,
> And yet cannot regret what it hath cost,
>   So dear is still the memory of that dream.'

Though we never touched, Mr. Ellis changed me, changed me utterly. His lessons became surrogates for my desires. Where I could not love, I learnt; I wanted to be the best I could be for my teacher. I got straight A*s, went to Oxford, and then to teacher training college – and all because of Mr. Ellis. It's a bit like Chantelle and Mr. Wickers, only with academic excellence. (The only thing Mr. Wickers can quote is the Fresh Prince of Bel-Air rap. And not even the long version.)

A few years later, once I'd joined Abbey Grove, I returned to my old school to thank Mr. Ellis for setting me on my career path, and maybe to consummate our love on the hockey pitch. But when I went into his classroom, I was stunned! There was Mr. Ellis. But he was no longer the handsome, beetle-browed, Dionysian poet, but rather a fat, tragic, coffee-stained depressive in a cheap suit, eating a sandwich made for him by his desperately lonely mother. Mr. Ellis was still Byronic, but that was only because Byron had a club foot and was subject to bouts of rapid weight gain.

Was this what Mr. Ellis had looked like all along? The youthful scales fell from my eyes. My devotion really had been blind! How could I have fancied him? I told myself that, in my innocence, I'd seen past these superficially unattractive things to the shining demigod beneath them. But then Mr. Ellis – by now smoking an unfiltered rollie – boasted, a seedy glint in his faded eye, that he used to steal my underwear from my gym bag. The final piece of the puzzle! I slapped him and stormed out.

Not for the last time, I'd been completely wrong about a man. And yet, though Ellis turned out to be a revolting and perverted troll, I cannot wholeheartedly hate him. So what if his teeth are now yellow? So what if he has subsequently been put on a register for sniffing the girls' bicycle seats? He taught me to love learning. And though I have to some extent lost state, station, heaven, mankind's and my own esteem, I do still have the memory of that dream.

So learn from my example. Fill out your UCAS careers form and remember, whatever you do, don't become a teacher just because you fancy one!

Careers Questionnaire

('aptitude means how good you are at a thing. So, for instance, if you didn't know what aptitude meant, put literacy at 6.')

Question 1:

Grade your academic strengths from 1-6, 1 standing for 'most aptitude' and 6 standing for 'least aptitude'.

Literacy

Mathematics

Sciences

Arts

Practical sciences (design technology, woodwork)

Sports

$1 - 2 - 3 - 4 - 5 - 6$

$1 - 2 - 3 - 4 - 5 - 6$

$1 - 2 - 3 - 4 - 5 - 6$

$1 - 2 - 3 - 4 - 5 - 6$

$1 - 2 - 3 - 4 - 5 - 6$

$1 - 2 - 3 - 4 - 5 - 6$

Question 2:

Name your three favourite subjects, in (ascending) order.

Going up

1. ...
2. ...
3. ...

(Don't say something like 'persimmon' or 'azure'. There are no medals for sounding like a dick.)

Question 3:

What is your favourite colour?

Question 4:

Do you want to join the Army?

Yes

No

Question 5:

List your three best characteristics, in descending order.

...

...

...

(handwritten: circle around "descending order" with arrow pointing left) Going down

Question 6:

If you've answered No to Q.4, have you seriously thought about it? I know all the wars we're fighting are pointless, but you get to make things go bang! Bang bang bang bang! Bang bang bang bang bang bang! It's really fun. Please? We only say 99% need not apply to sound cool. The government needs all the cannon fodder it can get.

Yes

No

From now on, you will be provided with a multiple choice of answers to each question. Circle which answer is most appropriate to you, then add up your score at the bottom of the questionnaire to discover your career of choice.

How would you describe your personality?

a) Not bothered.

b) Much-of-a-muchness.

c) I am a snowflake, unique unto myself. There are many like me, but none with exactly the same beautiful and miraculous intricacy.

What are your goals in life?

a) Not bothered.

b) I'd like to travel a bit.

c) I will become world-famous.

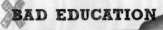

How happy are you to compromise all of your values?

a) Not bothered.

b) It depends what for. £60k+ and I'm yours.

c) I spit in your face. I am a snowflake, unique unto myself. I will never melt, or be mushed into a snowball which is then forced down the neck of the ginger kid who everyone bullies.

How prepared are you to spend a lifetime in a job you don't like, just because it's well paid?

a) Not bothered.

b) Quite prepared. Is there a secretary/co-worker I can flirt with? Only I'm trying to plan my midlife crisis now, so I can properly budget my divorce.

c) Snowflakes don't need money. I am an artist. Or maybe a 'creative', as it's a vaguer term. Basically, I'd like to work in advertising or telly.

Are you a good communicator?

a) Not at the moment – I need to get someone to jailbreak this iPhone I bought off a bloke down the pub.

b) Um, well, you know…

c) As Julius Caesar said, *fere libenter homines id quod volunt dredunt*.

If you were a city, which one would you be?

a) Swindon.

b) I'd prefer to be a nice suburb, like Kingston-upon-Thames.

c) Berlin.

How willing/able are you to take orders from a halfwit promoted over you on the basis of seniority?

a) What would you like me to say?

b) Careers are often a question of waiting your turn. Sure, I'd spend a while being bossed about by a twat. But give it fifteen years and I'll be the twat bossing around the next generation.

c) I only take orders from my muse. Her lofty eye and beguiling hips drive me ever on towards artistic triumph.

If you were a festival, which one would you be?

a) I can't put up a tent.

b) V Festival.

c) I make my own festivals. But if I didn't get all the licensing in place for my own festivals, I'd probably be Latitude because it's clever.

How happy would you be to drive a little car emblazoned with the logo of the estate agents for whom you spend long hours lying to newly married couples?

a) I can't drive.

b) Can I play fat tunes in the car? I'm thinking Ellie Goulding, Emile Sande and Mumford and Sons – those guys' dinner party anthems are euphoric!

c) Snowflakes can't drive. They can only be.

If you were a movie star, which one would you be?

a) Danny Dyer.

b) James McAvoy.

c) A French one.

If you had to have one celebrity's rider, which celeb would you choose?

a) 'Preferably there would be access to a toilet.' James Arthur.

b) 'Scotch eggs, sausage rolls and a six-pack of Tennent's in my dressing room, a party pack of Haribo, and a taxi home.' John Barrowman.

c) 'I demand a cellist to serenade me in my luxury suite, ten white puppies, ethically sourced vegan fois gras, sushi without the fish or the rice, vintage champagne, and a backing dancer I can take home with me.' Danny from The Script.

Results/Answers

Mostly a's... you're a worker bee, a drone content to follow without question even the most exploitative demands made on you by a greedy, charmless employer. The thought of independence terrifies you. All you ask for from life is a meagre wage to spend in the pub on a Friday night, flirting in a desultory fashion with the bored Estonian barwoman as you drink yourself into an early but not entirely unwelcome grave. You should become an agricultural labourer.

Mostly b's... you're an easy-come, easy-go person. You have modest but persistent dreams: a little house (for which you'll be crucified by the banks), 2.4 children (who will grow up to despise you), a second-hand car (in which you might decide to gas yourself), and a partner who is definitely having an affair with your best friend. You are content to live a lie because you feel that our society offers you no other alternative. You should become an agricultural labourer.

Mostly c's... you are someone with a proper sense of self-worth who will find it very hard to accept just how soul-crushing working in an office usually proves to be. A defiantly independent person, you're best suited to a career in which you are your own boss. You want to set your own hours, spend months being unemployed and even longer filling in your tax return. When you fall – and you will fall – you will fall hard. You should become an agricultural labourer. Or a palaeontologist.

8 October 2003

WATFORD OBSERVER

ONLY A PAWN IN THEIR GAME

BOY, 15, BREAKS LEG IN BIZARRE HUMAN CHESS INJURY

By Jessica Handes

A boy broke his leg during the Rickmansworth human chess match yesterday. Alfred Wickers, 15, was a pawn on the white side of the annual contest, watched by Rickmansworth's second-hand-car-tycoon-turned-mayor, Thomas Hare. In the very first move of the game, Wickers moved from D2 to D4. Witnesses describe him as making a kung-fu leap to the square, before landing badly and crumpling to the floor. An audible snap was heard, but Wickers – under the impression that his mother was in the audience – insisted on 'playing through the burn'.

Though Wickers' father, Martin, pointed out to him that his mother was, in fact, still 'in Spain with Javier and their children', Wickers refused to leave the field. Half an hour later, Wickers was called upon to move (or, rather, limp) from D4 to D5. By this time, his face was ashen, he was shaking and sweating in a manner onlookers could only describe as being 'truly horrific – like something out of *Trainspotting*.'

Matters came to a head in a few moves' time. A black bishop (played by Wickers' friend, Atticus Hoye), had moved within taking distance of the beleaguered white pawn. Wickers was ordered to kill his friend by moving diagonally onto E6. This he did on his hands and knees, but Hoye refused to die. A fight broke out between the

pawn and bishop; Hoye landed bodily on Wickers, and another crack was heard, even more sickening than the first.

Alfred and Hoye rolled around the chessboard, arms and legs locked together in a fatal dance, until Martin Wickers managed to pull the boys apart.

Alfred then staggered off the playing board to be violently sick onto the mayor's picnic. By now in the early stages of delirium, Wickers could be heard mumbling something about 'Mum's always watching Carlos, Lionel and Xavi playing their shitty games at shitty Spanish school'. He was then removed from the scene and taken by ambulance to Watford hospital, where – it is said – Atticus Hoye has spent night and day by his bedside.

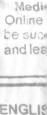

Dear Alfie,

Happy Christmas! I know it's March, but I'm a little bit behind the times because we celebrate Xmas a little later here in Spain. About one hour later, in fact, due to the time difference. Well, it's either an hour later or an hour earlier, but either way, it's confusing. Happy Birthday too! As I probably won't get that right.

Your semi-brothers Carlos, Lionel and Xavi are growing up so fast, and they are so tanned and healthy. That's thanks to Javier's DNA, I always say. I mean, look at the pasty mess your father and I made of you, ha ha!

How is school university (?) these days? We would love you to come and visit us in Spain. Just you wait till the guestroom is finished — I know it's taken five years, but it will be worth it, believe me! I know you said you don't mind sleeping on the sofa or in the little annexe by our infinity pool, but I want things to be just right for my Alfie!

Kind regards,
Mummy

PS Javier would like a word. Alfie, much thought of you, I will meet you a day soon, mi sol. Jav.

Alfie Wickers

21 Kiln Ro

Hertfo

HP

Alfie's recipe for a Tracy Island

I hav always wanted a Tracy Island from Thundrbirds. Attcus Hoyy has won cos his mummy and daddy bothered to ~~a~~ que for it when my mummy and daddy were gettin tipsie and shouting for fun like they do on ~~famly~~ family occazions, shoutin ysually about how stupid daddy's family is, that is my granny and grandpa who have ~~Christmas~~ Christmas with us. Anyway Atticusis Tracy Islan is amazin, the b est thing EVER EVER EVER. It's got sound afects and palm trees that go down and a little blue swimmin ~~pole~~ pool Thundaburd I come out of. Cos my parents ar poor, I cant have one, but Daddy say we should make our own won like they did on ~~Bloo Blu~~ Blue Peter.

So we got together a lot of ~~suff~~ stuff from his garrige, most of it is old and dampp and smells like my granny, but daddy said that was way cooler than silly plastic models. He said his daddy, grandpa, wouldnt like a plastic toy in the house anyway, cos it was probly made by the Japanees, who hit grandpa with shovels during the War. This is why grandpa don't have a toaster or telly, and refuses to see Dr Abdullah the really nice doctor who isn't Japanees but grandpa says is basically the same. Daddy says grandpa is a 'raceist', but when I repeeted this at Christmas lunch it was not a ~~popylar~~ popular thing to say. Neither was saying Dr Abdullah is a really nice man. Which he is, way nicer than grandpa. This also is not a ~~poylar~~ popular thing to say.

So the ingreedients you need for a Tracy Island is:

I CARDBORD BOX. We used the box the toaster came in which grandpa smashed with a shovel on Christmas day to show us what happened to him. Daddy and mummy say he ~~definitiley~~ ~~definatly~~ definitely wasn't hit by a Japanees man. Cos of his bad eyy-site, grandpa was acshuly a postman in Rickmansworth durin the War, but now he like to get tipsee and then talk 'shit' my mum says.

I LOAD OF PIPE CLEANERS. No one smokes a pype in my family, so we use loads of grandpas sigarett filters insted.

SOME PAPIER MACHAY. This we make from pva glue and grandpa's Daily Mail. Grandpa is not happy about us using his Daily Mail.

PAINT. You need lot of paint to paint over the Daily Mail with, otherwise mum say Tracy Island will be as raceist and deranged as grandpa, which I would not like. The Tracy family is a force for good the world over, not a lunatic old man with a plastic dummy's teeth cos he smoks so much.

IMAGINATION. My dad say this is pretty crucial, a s our Tracy Island wont be very like Atticusis with all the sound afects and palm trees.

We spend loads of time puttin all these ingreedients together listenin to daddy's ~~faverit~~ favourite man, Chris Rea. Sadly, it looks rubbish, as rubbish as Chris Rea. Just a blob painted green. Grandpa says it look like a 'space-age terd.' Bloo Peter is terd too.

I am very sad, so sad daddy drives to Watford that night and - MAGIC - the next day I wake up with a real plastic Tracy Island on the foot of my bed. Mummy is very cross, cos Daddy was drunk when he drove and has now lost his lisense, though I look all over the house for it. But she is ~~acshuly~~ actually not too angry when she sees me playing with Tracy Island all holiday with my daddy, who can't go anywhere cos we still havent found his lisense. Its the best Christmas ever.

Dear Mr and Mrs Keith-Roach,

My name is Alfie Wickers. You won't recognise the name, but you will probably recollect me from the things I did at your daughter Florence's sixteenth birthday party.

I'm incredibly sorry for vomiting into your Wellington boots. I hope only about three of them are complete write-offs. Compliments to the chef – I'd eaten a lot that night! That beef was so yummy, it even tasted good on the way out. And hey, look on the bright side – I left you with a couple of Beef Wellingtons! (I imagine you'll file that joke under the heading 'too soon'.)

If I can explain just a little bit . . . Florence said she'd be up for pulling me if I bought weed to the party. So I hung around in a place called 'Camden' until a man offered me some, which he was selling in individual Sainsbury's oregano pots.

To cut a long story short, it turns out the stuff Florence and I smoked was actually oregano. And with a lungful of oregano, your judgement goes out the window, a bit like your carriage clock, which I decided to defenestrate (I looked that word up especially to apologise – it means 'chuck through a windowpane').

So, yeah, sorry about the carriage clock. And the painting. And the telly. I hope all those things weren't as expensive as they looked! If it's any consolation, I wish I'd at least lobbed all that stuff out of the same window. I really didn't need to break more than one. But I guess that's what happens when you're tokin' the herb – logic gets flushed down the toilet. Like all your koi carp.

I forgot to say, you guys have got a pretty sweet house. They should do a Cribs on what's left of it.

The thing is, I've got a problem: when the sound system starts pumpin' out The Libertines, I go crazy. Pete Doherty and Carl Barât – the Ross and Rachel of my generation! Or at least they would be if there'd been a Friends episode called 'The One In Which Ross Breaks Into Rachel's Flat, Steals Everything, Smears "Artwork" On The Walls Using His Own Blood, Then Takes Up Crack In Prison.'

Finally, I'm also very sorry for getting into bed with you both. What happened was, I got really, really drunk and tried to get to second base with your daughter (post-Wellington boots) but she was shouting too much to let me. I can't remember a thing after about 10 p.m. Wshat Mr Keith-Roach told me on the way to the train station the next day, though, leads me to believe I should particularly apologise to you, Mrs Keith-Roach. I'm sorry for calling you mummy and crying into your bosoms.

I promise you'll never see me again,
Alfie Wickers

PS: Atticus Hoye punched your horse. He wasn't high, just in one of his black moods. Or maybe re-enacting his role in the school's production of Equus. Either way, you may want to get it checked out.

Stephen's Guide to Smileys

If a picture tells a thousand words, then a smiley tells 140 characters. And let's face it, if you can't say what you want to say in a single tweet, it ain't worth saying. Cheryl's tweets are honest, pithy and wise, like a modern-day Lily Allen (remember her?). Katie Price, on the other hand, goes way over the Twitter word-count when she's dissing Kelly Brook. Not cool. And FYI, @MissKatiePrice, for a double D mother of four, you're very quick to call other

Now, I'm sure you'll agree that the most important things you'll ever write are texts to your new BFs/GFs. What silly little novel could match the roller coaster of emotions you go through when you get a text from a guy/girl you've just started seeing? Apart from *Hunger Games*, that is.

But the crucial thing to remember about texting is this: don't run before you can walk. Hold off on the smileys, and ask yourself a basic but all-important question: how many kisses has your boo put at the end of their text, and what do those x's mean?

ONE KISS

This can go one of two ways. If they automatically put one kiss on the end of every text, then they're saying you're nothing special. Which you are – you a queen, Mrs. Carter! Uh-huh. So dump them, by text, quoting their ice-cold kiss right back at them like this: 'x'. If, on the other hand, they never usually put kisses in texts, then this one x is an uncomfortably intimate gesture for them. Uh-oh. He/she is emotionally 'special'. Maybe they were dropped on their heart as a child? And, if they can't feel, they're probably not worth it in the long run. Callous as it sounds, I'd advise you to dump them. But do it with a proper phone call (unless your plan is really weighted towards texting, in which case send an apologetic MMS).

TWO KISSES

The most infuriating number of all! I've known girls do this automatically, making xx mean nothing more than a full stop. The habit's rarer with guys, but it's not unknown. What it boils down to is

cross-referencing: does xx break or maintain a pattern? If it maintains, keep your distance. If it's a new development, then whoop-whoop! They're not the x-ing kind, so two kisses is a massive step for them. This date is in love and they ain't afraid to show it. They might be The One!

THREE KISSES

Woah! The triple-x is a minefield that even Diana, Queen of Hearts couldn't handle. The naïve textee gets three kisses and jumps for joy, but slow down, sista. It's seldom a BF texts a GF with xxx; for a happy couple, x does the job and xx shows you go the extra mile. If you've argued, then go all out with four, five or even six kisses. But three . . .? Call me a cynical old bitch, but three just don't ring true. Put it this way, a guy typing xxx isn't thinking of cuddles. He's thinking about what xxx sounds like said aloud. Which is 'sex' (though Mr. Wickers spent five minutes saying 'exexexexexexexex . . .' before he worked it out. God, he giggled. He still doesn't get why saying 'Norfolk and Chance' is rude, though.)

$;ΩP Flanter

This is a word my sister made up – a mash-up of 'flirt' + 'banter' to create 'flanter'. Flanter's when you're being funny, personal and even a little bit nasty, just to show the other person that you're really into them. The dollar sign is a kooky, winky head, full of brash wealth. The nose is a reference to Pinocchio – when people seduce you, they tend to go easy on the truth. The capital P suggests to me a tongue sticking out. Sexy or rude? You decide!

If I could go all the way back in time to the fiery, boyish Stephen Carmichael who started dating in summer 2012, I'd tell him to get to grips with the Text X before he even thought about sending a smiley. But I was young and fierce then. No one told me about the damage that one mistimed winking face can do to a relationship. We're talking nuclear-bomb-sized blast radius. We're talking the purple flares/Wookiee hair combo that destroyed Cheryl's career in America. Yeah, we're even talking what Angelina did to Jen.

Like La Hath in *Les Mis*, I learnt about love the hard way, at the School of Hard Knocks – coincidentally, the name of the school Miss Pickwell would like to start (only the knocks in her case would be literal, and applied using her bronze-tipped German Jungen-cudgel).

But luckily I'm in a position to help you, my little monsters. This a list of smileys for all occasions, from the happy first flushes of love to your messy public break-up. It's basically Harry Styles and Taylor Swift's story in a list of little faces. So buckle up – I've totally gone Gok on this.

@~)~~~~
A rose

Heaven! Although love is about pleasure and pain, petals and thorns, so try adding a ^ in the stem if a BF's being endearingly prickish.

(-}{-)
Kissing.

I got one of these when Joe Poulter took a girl dry-slope skiing at the Bassingbourn winter sports centre. I could cry right now remembering how beautiful this smiley looked on that fateful day!

:-# Braces

Your new honey may have a hot bod, but they also have a metal mouth. Oh, the irony – a smiley for someone who should never smile, for fear of blinding people with the light reflecting off their teeth, Anton Okwudo! This smiley can easily be switched with </3, the universal sign of a broken heart.

=^.^= Cat

This cutesy, Japanese-influenced symbol says 'Hello, Kitty!' to anyone who's being a bit bitchy, à la moi with that bit about braces (seriously, you won't regret dental work in the long run, Anton). The only question is, will the cat in question be able to text back with claws that big? I should flag up now that some boys do use this smiley to communicate a very different message, one to do with the number of ladies in the vicinity, so wires can get crossed. I remember being at a Parents' Evening once. Mrs. Poulter was saying something very unpleasant about Mr. Wickers' teaching

ability, so I texted him 'PTA =^.^='. Five minutes later, he burst in wearing his frightful hobbly shoes, because he thought I meant 'a load of single MILFS had turned up'. What a smutty mind.

=8) Pig

Chantelle and I have an agreement to send this smiley if one of us sees the other going on a carb binge in the canteen. It's a friendly warning sign between good-looking but weak-willed mates.

Σ8-O Cum face.

This is the ultimate, and it's all about clean, simple lines. Two popping eyes, the bold O, the little hat that looks like a crown – this smiley's king of the world, all right. Reserve it for sexts or really good flanter. As I say to my manicurist, if you've got to show your hand, show it in style.

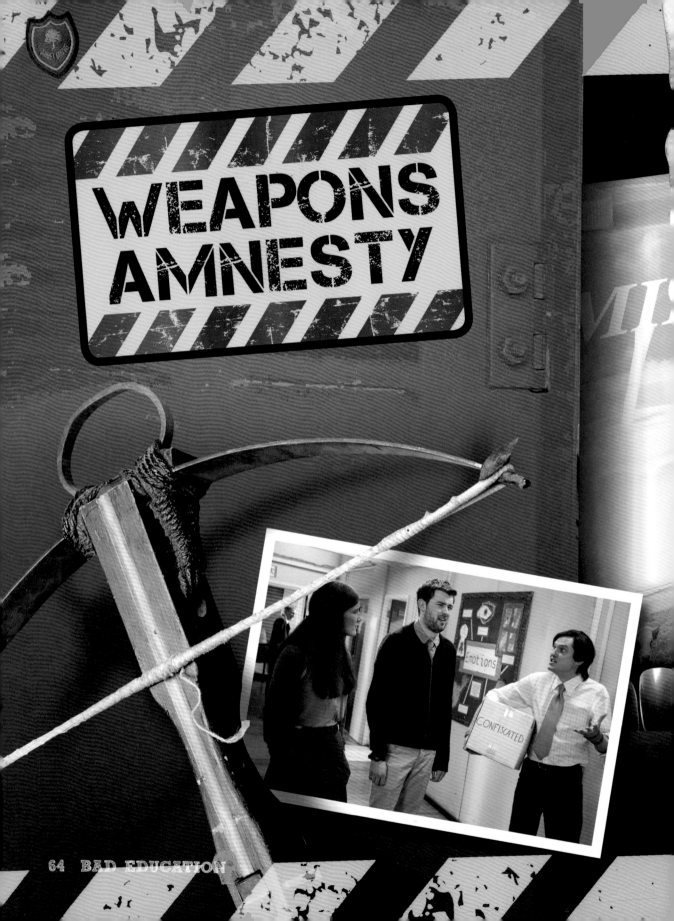

WEAPONS
AMNESTY

CONFISCATED

Emotions

Abbey Grove's
Come Dine With Me

Foreword by Shaquille Fraser

What makes a school tick, apart from Mitchell Harper's efforts to build a functioning time bomb? I'll tell you. The staff. And I count myself lucky to be the thug king of a mother-loving awesome posse. Yes, I know I'm *la grande vache qui rit*, but Captain Kirk needs a crew.

Miss Pickwell is Worf, my Klingon ensign: hideous, but efficient. Mr. Wickers is the fat little midget who rode around on Kirk's back in 'Plato's Children' (Season 3, Episode 10 – YouTube that Shi'ite, because it will blow your mind like a marketplace). Miss Gulliver, meanwhile, is pure Spock: highly intelligent, calm and collected, but essentially inhuman. After all, what hot-blooded, sentient earth-lady could refuse a taste of Frase Bentos pie? Nope, Miss Gulliver is an alien, probably from a ~~frigid~~ cold planet like Pluto or Hoth, the sixth planet in a remote system in the Outer Rim Territories, 50,250 miles from Core.

And yes, I did just mix *Star Wars* with *Star Trek*. Rule-breaking's in my DNA. My head's Kirk, my heart's Han Solo, and my body that of a white Lando Calrissian.

Anyway, when Worf, Spock and the fat little midget are getting on, all is well in Abbey Grove. It's a different story when they fight. And there was a battle royale two weeks ago. It started when Joe Poulter developed a skin condition. For legal reasons, I can't tell you exactly what happened. But suffice it to say that we broke a few laws to free Mr. Wickers from the gypsy doctor's canary-yellow caravan. Plus, the fighting-dogs ate Miss Pickwell's Bible, tarot became a playground craze, the biology lab's hamsters were made into sweetmeats, I couldn't move for child brides, and Joe's eczema *still* hadn't cleared up. Though I love good, old-fashioned magical folk, even I had to admit that Alf had gone a *little* too far.

The fall-out from gypsy-gate was so nuclear that I'm sure we'll all end up having three-headed babies. Apart from the asexual Miss Gulliver, of course, and Alfie and myself, being 'men' (though that didn't stop Arnold Schwarzenegger in an amazing documentary called *Junior*. Ex-Governor of California, male mother and twins with Danny DeVito? Miraculous man). And also Miss Pickwell, who probably bites off the heads of her mates *before* they've reached spoff o'clock.

As captain, leader, legend, it was up to me to heal the rift between the proud and haughty races of Klingon, Vulcan and fat little midget. My first attempt was taken from page one of the diplomacy rule book:

'Mariah,' I said to Isobel. 'Minaj,' I said to Alf. 'Chill the damnit down, cos where I'm cotching both yo booties look fine. Twitter's big enough for two behinds. And you, Azealia,' I said to Rosie, who thought she'd escaped my silver-tonguing. 'Don't be dissing no fat bitch, you feel? I love 212, but you been givin' all them dollars to Dominos? Girl, you *know* what I'm saying. Baby got *back*.' By this point, all three of them had left the common room.

If page one wasn't going to work, I'd have to rip up the whole effing rule book. And it was as I was ripping it up (not literally – I was ripping up some angry letters sent from Mr. Smith, a man of colour, asking me to refrain from talking to him like we were both in Compton circa 1993) that a brainwave crashed over me, dragging me into the undertow of a brilliant idea, filling my lungs with inspiration and making my entire life flash before my eyes.

How to make Isobel, Alfie and Rosie pals again? How else but to follow the example of Channel 4's screensaver, *Come Dine With Me*?

For those of you living on Hoth, *Come Dine With Me* has a very simple recipe:

Ingredients

1 boring, opinionated man

1 purse-mouthed spinster

1 drunk (ideally a female, as they're funny, whereas male drunks
are either threatening or tragic)

1 homosexual, mildly or wildly flamboyant (however much spice is needed
to rub up the boring, opinionated man the wrong way)

1 legend (i.e. fella in his mid-thirties, size five feet, wears a retainer
and maybe a helmet on windy days, collects *Trek* memorabilia and his
mother's dresses – very much headmaster material)

Instructions

Mix the ingredients up together, tempt them with a £1,000 carrot and whip them
with the stick of eating each other's appalling food in an atmosphere of lukewarm
conversation and barely concealed mutual hatred.

I couldn't think of a better team-bonding session. Certainly not after everyone
refused to do another sleepover in Madame Tussauds. And, FYI, I *obviously* wasn't going
to recommend doing that again. I'm still reeling from the cost of repairing the Miley
Cyrus waxwork (the PE teacher is a bit heavy-handed) and replacing the
Mrs. Thatcher, which Isobel 'liberated'.

So we embarked on the Abbey Grove *Come Dine With Me*. Over four evenings
last week, Alfie, Rosie G, P. Widdy and I wined and dined each other, to see if we
couldn't kiss and make up. Below are the match reports:

Cider at Rosie's –
by Shaquille Fraser

Rosie's dinner began badly when she forgot to send us her address. Or menus. Luckily, however, Alfie knew exactly where Rosie's flat was, and which shrub to stand behind in the dark park opposite her building in order to see inside her living room.

Alfie hastened to point out that he doesn't stalk Rosie (I believe him – how could he sneak around with those clumpy webbed feet?) but that he'd stood in this shrub with a rose in his mouth on Valentine's Day, waiting for Rosie to look out of her window. Sadly, she'd had a gentleman caller, so the curtains remained shut all night long. But that didn't put old Cyrano d'Wickers off! Only the early stages of dawn – and pneumonia – could persuade him to abandon his post. What a bloody romantic!

Rosie also hadn't told us if the dinner had a theme/dress code. And I've got to admit that, when Isobel joined Alf and me in the shrubbery, my heart fell to my gusset, becoming a third ball, or benign lump. To judge from Isobel's appearance, the theme was 'East European Dominatrix', and she'd *really* gone to town on the latex, mascara and exposed wintery flesh. By Shatner, I was going to look a fool!

When I complimented the efforts she'd taken to dress like a hollow-eyed sex worker, however, P. Widdy reassured me that this was her normal evening wear. The day was saved! I *wasn't* going to look like a bell-end in my open Hawaiian shirt, straw ten-gallon hat, denim hot pants and bare feet. (When in doubt, 'beach babe' is my go-to. It's cheap, cheerful and lets fresh air tickle all the bits and bobs usually caged by slacks.)

As she opened the door, Rosie's face was priceless. She must have practised that double-take for hours to make it look so natural.

Inside her flat, meanwhile, mein hostess made herself busy while Alf hovered in the kitchen door, promising to never employ travelling folk for their magical healing abilities ever again. Gypsy gate was still hanging in the air between them, heavier even than Isobel's candyfloss-and-bile perfume.

I spent about forty minutes providing a Dave Lamb commentary on Rosie's cooking, as everyone else drank heavily. R.Gul's technique was imprecise, almost like she was angry and flustered. In her haste, she even cocked up boiling peas. Peas! 'What a pea-nis!' I said, in the incessant nasal bark that scores the 34,069,455 hours of *Come Dine With Me* broadcast by Channel 4. Rosie, though, didn't laugh at my Dave Lamb shtick – weird how some people get so irritated by the things I find funny. Like the meerkat adverts, my last April Fool's on Alfie (why was getting 'Wickers' tattooed over my heart so 'weird'?), or Noel Fielding's Luxury Comedy. Come on, guys, Noel doesn't *need* to make sense! A purple badger who talks in oblongs? Comedy gold.

Rosie's menu was the biggest disappointment of the evening. For a starter, she served us crisps (organic, turnipy crisps at that – for me, it's Skips or nothing). For a main, a vegetarian moussaka with peas and salad. Isobel ate nothing; she refuses to touch food that hasn't been cooked in the blood of an animal. Alfie, quite drunk, sat gazing at Gulliver, also quite drunk. To cheer them up, I produced some sweetmeats the gypsy king sold me. This turned out to be a faux pas, and Rosie spoke with some warmth about how much her form had loved those hamsters. For pudding, we had coffee and a selection of local cab numbers.

By washing-up time, Alfie was so krunked he dropped all the plates. Rosie was not happy, even though – as Alfie pointed out – it's not his fault he's a sixteenth Greek. She sent us home at about 9.30. Alfie then claimed he'd lost his keys and he'd be sleeping on the street if Rosie didn't let him stay with her. I stepped in, saying he'd be welcome to twos my waterbed, but Alfie suddenly remembered his keys had been on his skater chain the whole time. What a space cadet!

Rosie's scores
Alfie gave her a 10, I gave her a 6, Isobel gave her a blood stained sack of mince the next day.

Wickers' Dinner –
by Isobel Pickwell

I can't think of anything I loathe more than Alfred Wickers. Even the Welfare State annoys me less. And yes, Mr. Fraser's a constant thorn in my side, though it's my belief that Abbey Grove's 'headmaster' is clinically subnormal. I take my lead from the unjustly sacked Glen Hoddle in assuming this disability to be the consequence of a sin Fraser committed in a previous life. To judge from the severity of his mental problems, I'd guess this sin to have been either murder or supporting the abolition of slavery – Fraser, that is, not Glen Hoddle. As it's now out of Fraser's hands, however, I'm predisposed to leniency.

Wickers' flat is as risible as its occupant. The fridge in his La-Z-Boy is stuffed with cans of Lilt, his cupboard is full of out-of-date protein shakes, and his walls bedecked with framed teenage posters. Does an alien smoking marijuana under the slogan 'Take Me To Your Dealer' require framing? I doubt it. Though maybe the floxie whose pendulous breasts are clothed in nothing more than gaffer tape does need an easy-to-wipe covering, given that Wickers is still a virgin.

Wickers told us that these posters once decorated the Middleton House dormitory in which he was bullied by those rich, snivelling whelps with whom he denies playing 'spunky biscuit'. And it was only daydreaming of him being made to act as a human darts board, or getting locked in a trunk overnight, that got me through what I can confidently call the second-worst evening of my life – trumped only by that dark, dark night of the soul when they hounded Mrs. T. from office. God knows what John Major's sinful spirit will be in his next life. A worm? A craven, brain-dead dog? Surely not a Fraser? Even I would find that rough justice.

Mr. Wickers is an unsophisticated brute. He insisted on sieving the wine I bought him – even though I told him the shards of broken glass were in there to bring out the flavour. In the end, we all preferred to stick to his 'cocktails'. On offer were Cheeky Vimtos (equal measures blue WKD and Lidl port) and Lad Juice (room-temperature lager, out of a 'bloke battery' – a can to you or I). I plumped for the Richard Littlejohn, a potent mix of port and sours. It tasted hideous, but at least Littlejohn's un-PC attitude is refreshing.

Because precious Rosemary Gulliver is a crank (read: vegetarian), Wickers had fixed on both a chicken starter and a chicken main for his dinner. He is obviously under the impression that chicken 'doesn't count'. Here, he and I are in agreement. Poultry does not run with blood; the meat is mere clucking *tofu*, a word I write under extreme duress, it being not only Asiatic, but symptomatic of the irreversible decline of Western civilization.

When Rosie explained that chicken is apparently considered a real meat, Mr. Wickers started a painfully flirtatious conversation about which came first, the chicken or the egg. I decided to join in with a little banter of my own, just to rain piss on his parade: 'However seductive she finds the philosophy, Mr. Wickers, with a face like yours I doubt that Rosie could come at all,' I told him, well pleased with my wit. He shot back with some nonsense about the existence or non-existence of my lady button, it having been worn to a nub in women's prison, but I ignored him.

The chicken starter and main were ruined by Wickers' inability to tell the time. The starter was burnt to a crisp, the main still red-raw after two hours of sitting in a bath of water, Wickers having tried to 'do a Heston'. At this point, I asked him to mix some of that broken glass into my drink, just to make the night pass quicker. Instead, he served us all ready meals: one Shanghai noodles, two spaghetti Bolognese and one plain egg fried rice. Gulliver called this 'microwave tapas', but her irksome optimism wasn't fooling me.

In the face of this failure, Wickers had the bad taste to invoke 'the Blitz spirit'. He implied we should make the best of a disaster. This set Fraser off imitating the sound of a Spitfire's engine. This didn't register with me, however, because I was too busy reeling from the painful family history that the phrase 'the Blitz spirit' will always conjure up. My grandfather, you see, was killed in the Blitz. The British scored a direct hit on his bomber.

Wickers' scores I gave him -2, Rosie gave him a 6 and Fraser a 7. The imbecile was impressed by Wickers producing both vanilla and mint-choc Viennettas for dessert, which Fraser promptly mashed up to create a 'Minty Vanilli'.

Isobelnacht –
by Alfie Wickers

Pickwell's got five Alsatians. Five! And they're all home-neutered. I'd seen them before on my one and only visit to her house, though that time it was only through the letter box I was holding open so Mitchell could Super Soaker laxative-laced Pedigree Chum around her hall. The dogs absolutely loved it. Pickwell did not, as she told me through gritted teeth. She can't prove anything, of course, but then she teaches Religious Education, so proof isn't at the top of her list of priorities.

Rosie, Fraser and I pushed Isobel's doorbell, which played a tinny version of the Horst Wessel Song until Pickwell opened the door with a face like racist thunder. In her hallway, Pickwell's got the Mrs T. waxwork she nicked from Madame Tussauds and the massive stuffed moose that she shot in British Columbia. She's also got a noticeboard with the house rules stuck up on it. They are:

- No running.
- No spitting.
- No petting.
- No shouting, except at socialists on *Newsnight*.
- No Irish, Jews or jazz.
- No trainers.

It turns out Pickwell also has a soundproofed cellar, which she says is for practising her tuba. One of her hobbies is playing in a local brass band made up of German ex-pats and what she called 'fellow travellers'. Seriously, the look she gave me when I asked if 'fellow travellers' meant she was part gypsy . . .

While we looked at her collection of ornamental weaponry, Pickwell brought us drinks that she'd prepared earlier. Because of her suspicions re the Super Soaker incident, and because I've seen a loads of *Poirot*, I swapped mine with Fraser's early doors, then excused myself to sieve my new glass just to be sure. I hadn't forgotten the broken glass.

For dinner, she gave us a beef fondue. Piles of juicy steak, served with sharp, long forks to dangle them into a boiling cauldron of red wine. I did try to look disapproving for Rosie's sake, but I don't think she believed my sad face because, to be honest, I couldn't bloody wait.

I soon realised why we were being treated to this meat feast, though. Every time I'd spear some steak and put it into the cauldron, Pickwell would take her sharp fork thing and jab me with it 'by mistake'. It was incredibly painful, worse than hearing Mitchell's rendition of 'Stay Another Day' by East 17, and that was bad enough to ruin roughly 60 per cent of my childhood memories. But I still ate loads. Plus, I got major brownie points for bringing along an aubergine for Rosie to eat.

While Pickwell cleared away the remnants of the fondue, I dared Fraser to have a go at riding her moose. Being a dickhead, he took literally no persuading. Unfortunately for Pickwell (and the moose), no sooner had Fraser hopped onto the moose than the laxatives that I *knew* Pickwell would've put in my drink took effect on him. Fraser's face went very white and his slacks went very, very wrong. Pickwell ran in to see him sliding off the moose's back and scurrying into the bathroom as Rosie and I tried not to laugh and/or be sick. The atmosphere wasn't helped by my joke about chocolate mousse being for dessert.

The night ended in Pickwell's bedroom. I imagine the last person who said that sentence is still eating through a tube, but we were lucky. Fraser sat on the white linen of Pickwell's bed pretending to give an interview to a fictional camera, while Rosie and I went through her knicker drawer. There was some scary shit in there. But not as scary as the stuff Pickwell was scraping off her moose.

I ended up feeling pretty bad for Pickwell, actually. I'd brought along some 'dog eggs' in a Tupperware to post through her door on my way out. But I decided that – in the circumstances – it would be too cruel.

I regretted this decision on the way home. After Fraser had waddled off into the night, Rosie caught the bus with me, even though it didn't go anywhere near her flat. I was in there! She even rested her head against my shoulder. Oi oi. Then she caught sight of the Tupperware in my bag. She asked what was in it and, thinking fast, I said, 'Just a snack.' She said she was famished – could she have it? I tried to stop her, but she insisted on opening the Tupperware. It was mostly awkward after that.

Isobel's scores I gave her 7 (it was really good steak), Rosie gave her 6 and Fraser gave her 10 by way of an apology for the moose.

Cotching with Shaq –
by Rosie Gulliver

(I'd like to point out that Fraser made me choose the title of this piece.)

I'm very open to new experiences. Ask my boyfriends. Or my girlfriends. However, even I was surprised when Fraser said that his *Come Dine With Me* was going to be an online affair. Isobel asked if Fraser'd ever had anything other than an online affair, except for that long-term relationship with his own right hand. Fraser corrected her by saying **'1) How was I to know Natalia, 19, from Gdansk was only marrying me for the visa, and 2) I'm actually left-handed.'**

(I'd also like to point out that Fraser has made me put his dialogue in Comic Sans because – quote – **'It most accurately reflects my warm but slightly off-centre chat.'**)

To be honest, the thought of us spending another evening together made me want to scream. But then Fraser dropped his bombshell. Or rather his **'Saracen-Orc's Wurlitzer shell,'** he joked (joked?). We were signing up to his favourite **'massive multiplayer'** fantasy war-gaming site, *World of Wizard War*, because his dinner would be served in the faraway digital Elf realm of Na'di Gogothen.

There was a long, long silence, broken only by Alfie asking to resign. But Fraser ploughed on: to get to the faraway digital Elf realm of Na'di Gogothen, Isobel, Alf and I had to play *World of Wizard War* with the characters he'd assigned us. My virtual avatar was a human princess, Alf's a hairy teddy-bear midget thing, and Isobel's a Slavering 'Dementrix'. By this point, Isobel was nearly in tears, Alfie was dry-heaving and I was completely baffled.

Fraser said we needed to earn forty experience points, measured in dwarf gold. We could do this by strafing the mountains of Barakkan, playing hooky with a Trystenthorpe witch, lunging into the Grey Forests of Fangroth, killing Lord Pernicio the Warlock, or paying $40 to a sun-starved Japanese twelve-year-old in exchange for some of the dwarf gold he harvests in his darkened bedroom.

'Young Aki's going to make a killing!' Fraser said. 'Wait, that's not a joke about Japanese schoolchildren becoming murderers. Though I do think, if there was one country where Hunger Games might actually come true, it's Japan.'

Fraser then told us a story about how he'd paid a substantial amount of money for a **'real life robot butler'** – confident in the knowledge that the Japanese **'can do anything these days'**. Unfortunately, the person selling this robot butler was the same man who hooked Fraser up with Natalia. Accordingly, six weeks after handing over his card details, Fraser received a cardboard box from **'The Robot Shop.'** Inside was a wan-looking, middle-aged Japanese man painted silver and wearing a tuxedo; Fraser saw through the disguise after about a week of Yamato jerkily carrying trays of drinks around and saying 'Affirmative, master' in a tinny voice. Apparently Yamato ended up getting a visa out of Fraser, too. Fraser's a fool, but he's a very accommodating one.

And Fraser was going to accommodate us in Na'di Gogothen, whether we wanted to be or not. He told us to **'Reconvene for vittles and good cheer once Morgana has danced the Sun bagatelle in the Na'di Gogothen firmament.'**

Which in practical terms meant me and Alfie ordering a Domino's at his flat before turning on our laptops about 8 p.m.

So that's why I found myself plodding around a computer graphicsy woodland, my avatar dressed like a Wiccan prostitute, Alfie's dressed like a furry, fat dog in a helmet and codpiece. Alfie and I were wearing headsets, which meant that we could be shouted at by pubescent sociopaths from around the world. The most common insults were 'nube', as in 'newbie'; 'larper', meaning someone better suited to Live Action Role-Play, i.e. dressing up like a wizard in real life; and 'bell-end'.

We found Fraser playing his pan pipe in a fictitious copse. His avatar is a faun called the Archbishop of Banterbury. Isobel was already in the copse, sharpening her strap-on sword. Fraser had laid out a **'feast'** of suckling dragon, many-moons pumpkins and otter-cakes, all of which were obviously not real. For the next hour, he made us sit staring at our screens making 'Mmmmnnnhh' noises into our stupid little headsets as our avatars ate food which, Fraser said, '. . . **cost an arm and a leg. Not mine - the little elf's when I was stealing her picnic! LOL. Turns out it was young Philippa Stamp from Form P. Unfortunately, I got a little carried away hexing her. Started using a bit of the old Wizard War slang.'**

'Like what?' I asked.

'Nube, larper, bell-end. I was shouting that last one down the microphone when I heard Philippa's mother in the background. The episode might come back to haunt me.'

After we'd eaten, Fraser made our characters play some games. The first was virtual Twister. Alfie's midget kept trying to slip a wand into my princess, so I hit him, spilling his Domino's garlic dipping sauce all over his keyboard. This made Alfie's character go a little haywire: he kept trying to mount Isobel, who had to be restrained with a freezing spell from killing him.

But Fraser had saved the worst till last. Caring for my beloved terrier in the last days of his life was less depressing than watching my princess, the teddy thing, the Dementrix and the faun dance the Harlem Shake.

The 'shaking' only stopped when Isobel's character slaughtered the Archbishop of Banterbury. Fraser was furious. However, Alfie and I were so delighted we bought Isobel a whole pig's worth of meat the next day. So, maybe *Come Dine With Me* did bring us back together? Though Fraser didn't talk to any of us for a week, in Comic Sans or otherwise.

Final scores

Fraser : 0
Alfie : 11
Rosie : 16 and a sack of mince
Pickwell : 23

Isobel wins 1,000 coins of dwarf gold! Which is lucky, because she's got hooked on *World of Wizard War,* and now rules Na'di Gogothen with a rod of iron.

FOREWORD BY ALFIE WICKERS

There is a saying that has been passed from teacher to teacher since the dawn of time. From the monks of the Dark Ages, drumming the minutiae of biblical law into their novices, via the mutton-chopped Utilitarian pedagogues of the nineteenth century, all the way to the rudderless graduates who resentfully fall into teaching today, this saying has informed education throughout the history of modern civilication. In times of great need, it helps us cope with the very worst students in our care. Like a bucket of water travelling up a line of pre-hose firemen, or an empty bucket being passed around at London Fashion Week, or a bottle of gin going from dressing room to dressing room backstage at the Loose Women studio, this saying is a lifesaver. And thus I bequeath it to you:

'If they're shit at absolutely everything, make them take up Art.'

Truly, wisdom of the ancients. But why has it proved to be so useful, throughout my long career teaching class after class of window-licking nut jobs?

Because Art is 'subjective'.

Just as one man's terrorist is another man's freedom fighter, so too is one man's piece of shit another man's Mona Lisa. Unlike in annoying subjects like Maths, no one can tell an artist that their work is definitely wrong. Yes, Tracey Emin looks like she's an egomaniacal tax dodger. And yes, Damien Hirst looks like a greedy, derivative shadow of his former self. But you can't say that these artists definitely are these things, because everything is open to multiple interpretations. Maybe they're just playing at being has-beens, in order to provoke an analysis of the ideologico-aesthetic bourgeoisie? If that sounds like bullshit, it's because it is bullshit, but that's the point. Any mug can flunk Art and get away with it. And here is a case in point . . .

Rem Dogg is not an excellent student. He has never owned a pencil case. He has never bothered to read even the Spark Notes of a book he's studying. When asked what To Kill A Mockingbird was about, Rem Dogg said that it was a self-help book about blokes getting over break-ups, written by Danny Dyer.

While the last time I made him sit a mock History exam, when Rem Dogg was set the essay question: 'Who, in your opinion, caused the English Civil War?' he wrote, 'Your mum,' then sat back and texted for the next two hours.

Nor does he have a great record with the arts. On a school trip to the theatre, Rem Dogg shot War Horse's puppeteer with a gas-powered BB gun, explaining that they kill horses when they fall over at the Grand National 'and getting tangled in barbed wire's basically the same shit, innit.' I had to physically push Rem Dogg out of the fire escape before the police arrived, but not before he called an old lady usher 'a bender'.

However, the law states that Rem Dogg must pass a certain number of GCSEs. So, Art it is. This is lucky, because Rem spends most of his time in class drawing pictures of me doing unmentionable things to livestock. They're not very good pictures, but strangely the childlike understanding of them makes them all the more unpleasant. I've tried to turn this into a positive by suggesting that Rem become a painter or an illustrator. And, though he thinks that both those professions are – quote – 'gay', Rem Dogg takes my point re piss-easy exams. I mean, even Prince Harry got a B in Art A-level. Though, to be fair, he did have a teacher cheat on his coursework for him. Ah, the benefits of a private education . . .

Anyway, Rem Dogg has just finished his first year of Art and I am very proud to present to you the fruits of his labours. Yes, certain people may think that a single A4 piece of paper doesn't look like a year's work. And, yes, maybe its minimalist aesthetic looks easy. And possibly the story does seem quite disturbing. But remember, this is Art. A* for that man, I say.

I give you, The Dark Dogg Rises: A Grafic Novil, by Leslie 'Rem Dogg' Remmington.

Abbey Grove Football Tactics

I'll be honest, I've not played much football. At Middleton House, we played rugby in the Michaelmas Term, hockey over Lent and cricket in the summer. I say 'we', I mean the rest of the school. I tended to duck out of sport by going to the school nurse with a new and fairly serious fake illness each year.

When I was thirteen, I pretended that I had gout. But it turns out that *everyone* at my public school has gout. Must be all that swan-meat and pâté. To stand out from the crowd, I had to 'catch' TB. This was easy – it's just coughing and maybe a dash of ketchup around the lips. At fourteen, I developed scurvy; every week, I'd paint my teeth black and talk like a pirate to the bored nurse. By fifteen, I was getting ambitious. Rickets spread my wings. I would walk into the school sanatorium wearing calipers and holding a sooted chimney-sweep's brush, offering to do their stacks for a sovereign, m'lud. The rickets act was so convincing that the nurse said I didn't need to come back for check-ups. She said this was because I could be contagious. With hindsight, though, I suspect she maybe just found me irritating.

Unfortunately, that nurse left in the summer after my GCSEs. She was replaced by a Nurse Ratchedy harridan of about fifty, a she-wolf seemingly bent on destroying my life. I'll never forget Ratched peeling off my fancy-dress lesions on the first day of the new term. She'd seen it all, she said, before making me donate three pints of blood to the cat sanctuary in case any other pussies got ill. Then she turfed me out onto the rugby pitch, where I spent four hours in sleet, retching from blood loss at every bone-crunching tackle.

I could see that Holmes (me) had met his Moriarty (her). I seem to anger women like Ratched, who was basically just Pickwell but English and menopausal. If anything, Ratched's hot flushes made her even more terrifying than P. Widdy. Anyway, shit had just got real at Middleton House. Well, I could handle that.

Next week, I strode into the sanatorium and declared that I had a benign tumour on my hip. And there genuinely *was* a lump there, though it was actually just a fatty deposit. I know this because my chocoholic dad has one – after

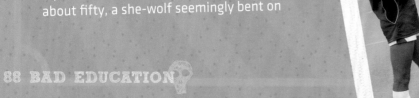

thirty years of eating a Kit Kat a day, his fatty deposit's reached the size of a terrier's ball, swinging from his upper leg. With Martin Wickers' DNA, who needs enemies?

After half an hour spent trying to twist the 'fake' lump off me, Ratched had to concede that it was real. Though I'd gone through agony, I knew that I'd won. The thing about school nurses is that they're basically idiots. You could have an axe sticking out of your head, and the average school nurse would wrap a Tubi-grip round your knee then send you home with half a pack of Strepsils. Nurse Ratched was only different in the respect that, given half a chance, she'd have driven the axe into my head *before* giving me the textbook Tubi grip/Strepsil one-two.

One-two – bit of football chat. Don't worry. There's more where that came from. 'Man on!' 'Tiki-taka!' 'The teenage girl's pressing charges, lads!' Classic.

For the next two terms, I pretended that my lump was being treated privately. But then Ratched forced my hand: either my 'private doctor' removed the benign tumour, or she would send me to Watford hospital to have it cut out by the NHS. Well, I couldn't pretend my fatty deposit had been removed, because it would still be there when she checked. And obviously I couldn't actually afford BUPA. The bitch had me by the Ashley Cole (which, I believe, is slang for 'penis').

I was forced to go to Watford. Ratched came too, just to watch.

Just before the anaesthetist put me under, I asked if the surgeons could cut into my leg in the shape of a question mark, so I ended up with a cool scar. The rather grumpy anaesthetist said no, jammed the mask on my face and told me to count to ten.

'If a question mark's too hard, could I have it in the shape of an A? Either capitals or lower case – up to you. Any font except Comic Sans,' I said, trying to be reasonable. The anaesthetist turned up the dosage; gas was now pouring down my throat. 'Not an A, then. An exclamation mark? That's just a line with a little extra dot at the why doesn't mummy love me, sodding Javier, like a shitty elephant in the circus all like woo I can fly I'm Spanish well I hope they run out of peanuts Dumbo...'

The gas had taken effect. Thirty more seconds of subconscious gibberish and then the next thing I knew Nurse Ratched was visiting me in my hospital bed. She said she hoped I didn't mind, but she'd had my lump set into a paperweight.

I thought she was joking, but it was sat there on her desk at the beginning of next year when I went in to tell her I'd contracted syphilis. And again she didn't believe me, even though I came in with tin foil over my nose like Johnny Depp has in *The Libertine*. She said she'd worked in a women's asylum before transferring to Middleton House, but had never yet encountered a woman crazy enough to sleep with me. In the end, I just got Atticus Hoye to push me down a flight of steps so that I broke my arm. No games for me. So who won that one, Ratched? Fractured tibia over here, that's who!

All that's a long way of saying that this Saturday is the annual football match against Middleton House. It's become tradition for me to manage the Abbey Grove squad in the build-up to the game, ever since the PE teacher did a Rolf Harris and took up the didgeridoo. But what qualifies me to coach you lot? What makes me the Special One? Well, I'll tell you.

I've got *faith* in you guys. Despite the fact that Rem Dogg's in the team and he's not even our worst player. In fact, he's the only one who seems to be able to win a header, usually by running over the toes of his opposite man.

Last year, the referee expressed some doubt over Remmy needing to stud his wheels with nails, but how else was he going to get a grip on the Astro Turf? Anyway, it was cool, I explained to the ref (that four-eyed twat – bit of banter there, about referees always having glasses... that's right, isn't it?). Rem Dogg's chair was like something out of Gorkamorka. When the ref acted dumb, I explained that Gorkamorka was a Warhammer 40K spin-off based on a *Death Race*-style sport on the desert Orc-populated world of Angelis. Infuriated by his blank face, I appealed to the players.

'Gorkamorka? Warhammer? The desert world of Angelis?' I said, my arms outstretched. 'No one knows what I'm talking about? Jesus, the kids today.'

All the players were staring, and the crowd had begun to slow-clap. Slow-clap the ref, that is. I'm sure those empty cans were meant to hit old '20-20 vision' and not me.

child with frostbite but all I've got to do is bung the lads on that pitch, wave in the direction of the opposition's goalmouth and you guys will do the rest. Believe.

⚽ I'm also motivated by revenge for all the years of playful abuse I received at my old school. That's why these Middleton-Grove grudge matches tend to get pretty rough. But don't let the violence – or my relative newness to the beautiful game – deceive you. There's some major tactical nous behind Abbey Grove United. Mitchell Harper's got some ideas he says are gonna help us thrash Middleton. So, with no further ado, I'll hand over to my very own David Platt. 'On the head-the-balls, guv'nor!' 'Stand up, it's a man's game!' 'Engine room.'

⚽ So I've got the passion. I can scream 'THIS IS *SPARTA*!' with the best of them, and I don't even mind doing it in a loincloth if it'll inspire the sweeper (Chantelle). What I don't have is the tactics. But then, the modern game is too reliant on clipboards, formations and stats. I'm old-fashioned, like a less puce-faced Harry Redknapp. I may write like a

As he says, Wickers didn't play football. He was too busy making the other boy wizards drink his potions in the dormitories of Griffindick Tower. So I've given him some real tactical advice, like making the Abbey Grove lot tackle in the style of Paul Scholes. God may have beaten him with ugly stick to the point of senselessness, but Scholesy was the bollocks when it comes to the high, studs-up challenge. Less the Ginger Xaxi, more the Ginger Bruce Lee.

Middleton House is basically Hertfordshire's under-18 county team. They got all the money behind them, plus some pretty amazing talent. Our secret weapon, though, is Abbey Grove's synchronised diving squad. They may have crap ball skills but – when it comes to dives – they're almost as good as Gareth Bale.

But if I've tried to teach Wickers one thing, it's that a manager can do all the spreadsheets and tactical formations he wants. At the end of the day, though, it's the fans who win the match. If your supporters create the right atmosphere, it's game over. So I've drawn up some tactical styles for the fans, based on big Premier League clubs, that the Abbey Grove lot can do in the crowd on Saturday. Check it.

LIVERPOOL This tactical style is based on passive aggression. The aim is to bore the opposition into defeat. Make sure you whinge about the glory days back in the 70s, when men wore moustaches and had women's hair, then get well uppity if anyone don't understand your accent. Basically, Liverpool fans are like your nan: whiny, repetitive and bitter.

Bring: nostalgia.

ARSENAL Wickers is a classic Gooner, i.e. a posh bender. Arsenal fans are masochists, and 'masochism' means all that weird stuff with ropes, whips and latex masks Rem Dogg watches on his phone (the kind of thing Miss Pickwell wants to do to Wickers, only without the safe word. Or the sex). Gooners try and prove their team ain't rubbish by quoting loads of bullshit about the transfer market. 'We're the only solvent team in the Premiership!' they boast. Only they don't boast in their stadium, which remains icily silent at all times because loud voices are

WEST HAM If you're a West Ham fan, you're a gentleman. Yeah, there might be a scrap or two along the way, but it's all good stuff. Just a couple hundred geezers glassing each other from either side of a pathetic police cordon. It's about respect, it's about history, it's about passion.

Bring: knuckledusters, a small knife, a hoarse voice for shouting *Blowing Bubbles* and a photo of your old mum cos you're good to her. Also, bring me. My dad's banned from the grounds (don't ask – you gotta do some dark shit to get banned from the 'Ammers) so I got no one to go with since Rem Dogg's parents stopped me using his disability to queue-barge. Rem Dogg's dad is such a nonce, man. No wonder he got a glass eye.

fined £3,500. If you guys act like Gooners, the opposition fans will be so disgusted by the match-day atmosphere they probably won't bother turning up.

Bring: your calculator, to help you work out how much you need to borrow from Wonga to buy a pint at the Emirates. You can also type some rude words on a calculator if you hold it upside down, which is about all the fun you're gonna get at a Gunners game.

CHELSEA Playing as a fan of the Chelse, you gotta imitate your hero, John Terry, and the robust language he directs at certain players. The Blues pretend to be well hard, but they're still little bitches who'd bend themselves over a barrel for Roman Abramovich. Chelsea fans are like Chantelle: you've had loads of blokes coming and going, but all you dream about is the Special One. In Chelsea's case, it's Jose Mourhino. In Chantelle's, it's that dipshit Wickers.

Bring: a banner saying *Captain, Leader, Legend* and the excuse, 'I've got a [insert racial minority] friend!'

THIS ITEM WAS recovered from the disastrous field trip Mr. Wickers and Miss Gulliver led to the Tring Petting Zoo & Ink Museum. For transport, they employed Sunshine Swing Holidays, having received a tip-off from the 80+ Miss Mollinson, who'd been repeatedly satisfied on a Sunshine Swing package trip around the stud farms of Germany.

It turns out, though, that this Sunshine Swing company is as sordid as they come. And they do come, which is why the company guarantees to 'sluice down' each coach between trips, the seats are wrapped in plastic, and those little ashtrays are very sticky to open. Be warned: jemmy them open with gloves.

Nevertheless, Mr. Wickers and Miss Gulliver felt that Sunshine Swing offered an appropriate environment for children! Oh, they protested their innocence, of course, when parents asked why their children smelled like they'd spent all day in a men-only sauna. But had 'Gulfie' bothered to research Sunshine Swing (instead of trusting a pensionable slapper like Miss Mollinson), they'd have doubtless discovered the company's depravity for themselves. Because Sunshine Swing are not shy when it comes to publicising their revolting modus operandi, as the affixed brochure demonstrates.

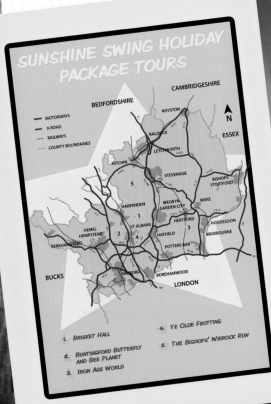

SUNSHINE SWING HOLIDAY PACKAGE TOURS

CAMBRIDGESHIRE

BEDFORDSHIRE

ESSEX

— MOTORWAYS
— A ROAD
— RAILWAYS
— COUNTY BOUNDARIES

ROYSTON

BALDOCK

LETCHWORTH

HITCHIN

STEVENAGE

BISHOPS STORTFORD

5

HARPENDEN

WELWYN GARDEN CITY

WARE

ST ALBANS

HERTFORD

HODDESDON

1

HEMEL HEMPSTEAD

2

4

3

HATFIELD

BROXBOURNE

BERKHAMSTEAD

POTTERS BAR

BUCKS

WATFORD

BOREHAMWOOD

LONDON

1. BRISKET HALL
2. BUNTINGFORD BUTTERFLY AND BEE PLANET
3. IRON AGE WORLD
4. YE OLDE FROTTING
5. THE BISHOPS' WIRROCK RUN

SUNSHINE SWING HOLIDAYS

HERTS-BREAKER TOUR

'Hello, boys and girls. Paul Rustle here, your extra-friendly coach driver. Welcome to Sunshine Swing's brand new Herts-Breaker Tour™. We are passionate about finding anonymous sex solutions for our clients, which is why our coaches now run a dedicated dogging service around Hertfordshire.

When it comes to no-strings whoopee with one or more overweight strangers inside a series of filthy commercial vehicles, Hertfordshire is the thinking man's Rutland! Or Rut-Land, more like! Yup, there'll be jokes ten-a-penny from me, your friendly MC at the front. 'What do you call a black milkman?' 'What did the Arab say to the cat?' 'Why did my mother-in-law think I was Jewish?' Classic gags all the way from the Embassy Club and a more innocent time.

So sit back and relax as I take you up the A-Road, or maybe even the B-Road for a tighter, single-lane adventure into the muddy unknown!

BRISKET HALL – a stone's throw from Welwyn Garden City and built for Sir Matthew Lamb, 1st Baronet, in around 1760, this magnificent stately home can be glimpsed between the trees of Bluebell Hill Wood. A short, picturesque walk from the B653, the wood provides natural cover for any group action that can't fit in the back of a stripped-out transit.

BUNTINGFORD BUTTERFLY AND BEE PLANET – Hertfordshire's own Eden Project, this butterfly land has got more than enough to keep the average visitor busy for hours. Perfect for us! It's amazing how publicly you can hatch your trouser-chrysalis when the civilians are rubbernecking what are basically gay wasps.

IRON AGE WORLD – an Iron Age adventure park just off the otherwise pretty dry A10. Here, out-of-work actors dress in leather jerkins and chuck stones about outside turd-strewn goat-sheds. Apparently, this is what the Iron Age was like, although (to my eyes) it looks a lot like modern-day Scotland. The centre's got some very horny archers, storytellers and woodsmen knocking around after closing time, and that's when we scoop em up! Fancy shagging a Neanderthal in a car park, but don't want to slog all the way to Sugar Hut in Essex? Look no further.

YE OLDE FROTTING BOARS – one of the oldest pubs in Britain, this joint boasts glory holes cut by poniard-carrying perverts from the 1440s. Do it like they do it on the History Channel! Be warned, though: this pub is in the suburbs of St. Albans, so keep your bestial grunting to the bare minimum.

THE BISHOPS' WIRROCK RUN – this is my favourite route in all of Herts. Starting in the hamlet of King's Walden, we cruise down Lilley Bottom Road (no lily-livered bottoms welcome on my coach!) to the how's-your-father one-two of Duck Trap Wood and Bigg's Grove. We then skip Coldicote (too many kids) to pass Welwyn on the A1. On good days, I like to hit the hazards round Welwyn's antique round-about – supposedly the oldest in the UK – so we can have a quick fiddle on a bit of history! And we finish each other off in a lay-by off the A1 around North Mimms on the Water End Road. Water way to End the trip, I say! Particularly if it's golden shower Wednesday.

'When I'm not busy shouting in Albert Square, I like to let my hair down on a Sunshine Swing holiday. Not that I've got any hair.' MYSTERY CELEB

'When I'm not being a pundit of BBC 5 Live, or briefly starring in the film Basic Instinct 2, or regretting incidents caused by my quick temper, I like to let my hair down on a Sunshine Swing holiday. Not that I've got much hair.' MYSTERY CELEB

I found these in my pigeonhole the morning after the Abbey Grove staff Christmas party. They were unsigned, but it doesn't take an intellect of Dr. Goebbels' stature to sniff out the competitors – if 'sniff' is the word I want, which it probably isn't, given the orifices on display.

I'd suggest that the Thunderbirds belong to Mr. Wickers. Wickers once boasted to me that he'd never bought his own pants, instead receiving a yearly supplement of three 'fun' pairs in his stocking at Christmas. These were purchased for him by his mother, until she eloped to Spain with a greaseball named Javier. Wickers' father has since taken up the undercracker cudgel. It is beyond me to speculate as to whether Wickers Senior or his sex-crazed ex-wife purchased the pair in question. But I can say that there is very little that's 'F.A.B.' inside them – Alfie's Thunderbird 1 has famously never achieved lift-off, at least with a lady.

The second posterior is even easier to place. It is common knowledge that Mr. Fraser started a company that specialises in customised velour underwear. He went as far as to take this company, 'Sweet Cheeks', onto Dragons' Den, but he lost out to a man who invented flexible Tupperware. However, this was only the start of his troubles, having invested in the 'juicy' phenomenon six months ago, long after the veloured bubble-butt burst. Unable to compete in the marketplace, Fraser has been left with a lock-up garage full of velour Y-fronts, brassieres and garters, which he's been reduced to selling around the school. Buyers are able to specify what words they want written across their behinds and/or breasts, because Fraser has turned detention into a kind of sweatshop. With naughty children stitching clothes for an hour every morning, his company's probably making a packet, even if he is his own (and most probably only) customer.

5. Form K's snowmen

This winter, the unusually heavy snowfall made it almost impossible for even an old stager like Isobel Pickwell to maintain discipline. Luckily, I have one seasonal procedure that keeps the lid on things. If children are misbehaving, I throw my own brand of snowball at them, snowballs which have some different 'secret ingredients' concealed at their centre. I call them Snow Revels, though I doubt you'd want to put my balls in your mouth. In some of them, I put small stones. In others, rotten tomatoes, canteen curry and bits of broken glass.

If there are any dead birds to hand, all the better. Robin Redbreast's corpse makes quite an impact on the younger tearaways, caught as they are between teenage delinquency and the last globules of milky, sentimental childhood.

Though my Snow Revels managed to control even Frank Grayson, there's always a Mr. Wickers-shaped fly in the mulligatawny. It turns out that he and his form snuck back into the playground after I'd knocked off for an evening spent throwing eggs at a family-planning clinic. The next day, I discovered what they'd been up to, namely a grotesque and subversive tableau of snowmen right in front of Abbey Grove's main entrance.

This is perhaps the least offensive set of snowmen. Here we see a triptych of Whitney Houstons through the ages. First is Whitney as she was in 1985. Last is Whitney in all her Bodyguard glory. In the middle, it's Whitney as she was for 1990's 'I'm Your Baby Tonight'.

That album contains 'My Name Is Not Susan', the only Houston song I like. Why? Because my twin sister is called Susan. She was always the 'fun' one when we were growing up, a cheerful, coquettish child who held our ridiculous parents in the palm of her grasping hand. I've been forced to say 'My name is not Susan' countless times, to teachers, postmen, (her) friends, lecherous village boys, and senile relations. The response is always the same. When they discover that I'm Isobel, the smiles tumble from their faces like meat off a lamb shank.

I should say that Susan isn't all bad. The line 'My name is Susan' has come in handy once or twice when the police have been questioning me in connection to a spate of arson attacks aimed at Oxfam bookshops. So thanks, Susan, and sorry about the legal bills.

Underneath the Whitneys, meanwhile, are the words 'carpe diem', presumably to suggest that Houston's soul may melt to naught but that, in her day, she lived a fierce and full life. Given this saccharine message – and the impressive level of detail put into the Whitneys' hair, clothing and accessories – I'd put my money on Stephen Carmichael and Chantelle Parsons being responsible for the Whitney triptych.

here we have a series of indecent snowpeople. I assume they're the work of Mitchell Harper and Leslie 'Rem Dogg' Remmington, given the tyre-marks and Doc Martins footprints preserved overnight in the snow. In Figure One, we see a snowman copping a feel of a snowlady's bosoms from over the top of an Abbey Grove jumper. This is known by our pupils as 'second base'.

Figure Two, we see the snowman and snowlady doing what I'm informed is called 'dagganing', whereby the lady provocatively grinds her posterior against the man, as they doubtless do in Hertfordshire's steamier nightclubs and discothèques. Hence, I assume, the Rastafarian snowman DJing at a snow-soundsystem behind the dancing couple. Figure 3, meanwhile, is the worst of

the bunch – the lady lies on top of the man in a kind of top-to-tail which I know as the 69 (I was young once). It took several trips with the boiled staffroom kettle to destroy Figure 3, so engorged had the snowmale become.

Beholding these monstrosities, I felt like the Victorian archaeologists who chanced upon the artwork of Ancient Rome – the Romans took a similarly schoolboyish pleasure in phalli. Those same Victorians coined the word 'pornography' to describe the horrible paintings and sculptures they excavated from the ruins of Pompeii by Mount Vesuvius. I myself feel that 'pornography' is too soft a word to apply to these degraded manifestations of Form K's crazed imaginations.

This last snow-disaster is, I take it, meant to resemble me. My willowy figure has been elongated, my proud jawline blown out of all proportion and I have fangs everywhere. I must say that its structural integrity is fairly impressive. This I put down to Jing Hua, of course. I imagine that she took care of the technical aspects of the creation while Wickers supervised the aesthetics.

I also imagine Joe Poulter was in on the act, if only because he follows Wickers around like the runt of a litter tailing his mother: tongue out, slouching, and all dumb, eager eyes. Yes, they must have had quite a laugh with this one. Well, let's see who's laughing after Grayson helps me pelt them with some particularly foul Snow Revels.

I think this speaks for itself.

HERTFORDSHIRE COUNTY COUNCIL
EDUCATION COMMITTEE

REPORT BOOK

Reports will be entered at the end of each
school year, where the book will be sent to
parents for inspection, signature AND RETURN

ABBEY GROVE SCHOOL
HERTFORDSHIRE

Headmaster: S FRASER

Report Card

Name: Chantelle Parsons

Form behaviour:

Say what you like about Chantelle — and graffiti around Abbey Grove shows you can say an awful lot — but she *is* always paying attention. Her eyes are fixed on me pretty much from 8.30am to almost 7pm every single day, unlike the rest of the class. For the simple reason that none of them follow me home after school finishes at 5.

That said, I think she's looking in the wrong place. And I don't just mean when she's rifling through my dustbin. I don't want to specify what she seems to be staring at, but let's just say it's not my face.

Or my torso. Or my arms. Or my feet. Or my shins.

Frankly, Chantelle's intimidating behaviour is self-defeating. Though her eyes are warm, the effect is chilling, like stepping waist-deep into a cold lake or sea. By the end of a double period, there's very little for her to look at, even when I'm wearing white jeans à la Marvin from JLS.

Her flirting has turned me into a die-hard Europhile (which, to be clear, Chantelle, does not refer to French kissing, generous portions of body hair or German water sports). Last term, she would frequently touch me as I passed her in the classroom, the corridor, or in the darkened hallway of my flat. Each time she did so, I would remind her — in a shaky, panicky voice — of 'the six-inch rule'. To this, she'd unfailing reply that 'I won't be breaking that, sir. You look like an eight or nine.' Terrifying.

Unlike beer and milk, however, penises are not exempt from the EU's metric system. Therefore, the six-inch rule is now technically the 15.24 centimetre rule. And, when I remind her of 'the 15.24 centimetre rule', Chantelle is baffled — she can't picture a willy in centimetres. So she's given up making crude remarks. Result!

Though she is still touching me. Please, Mrs. Parsons, can you make her stop?

History class:

At the start of term, Chantelle was particularly hot for on the Tudors. She cooled off when I explained that Henry VIII didn't actually look like Jonathan Rhys Meyers, more like the Geography teacher after an all-you-can-eat meat buffet.

More generally, I'm always surprised by Chantelle's ability to find innuendo in any historical subject, however dry. Her suggestion that I could repeal her Corn Law was a little inappropriate; her 'sexy' riff on the Cuban Missile Crisis (something along the lines of concealed warheads and back-door diplomacy) left me a nervous, gibbering wreck.

Chantelle never does her homework. I once got annoyed about this. Was she really so busy that she couldn't write a 500-word essay? In hindsight, I can see that the question 'Did you have your hands full with something really massive last night?' was just asking for trouble.

Name: Leslie Remmington

Form behaviour:

Leslie — or Rem Dogg to everyone here at Abbey Grove — loves making me feel like I'm walking on eggshells. Not least when I told him this. He said that 'walking on eggshells' is 'wheelophobe'. Leslie often uses his disability against me like this. Honestly, sometimes I wish I could just clamp your son. Though obviously that sentence doesn't look good in black and white.

Leslie and I have a healthy level of banter going on, which I think shows a mutual teacher-pupil respect. He calls me Professor Dumbledick, Count Dickula, The Artist Formerly Known As Dick, All Dick And No Dom, and Made In Chelsea. I, meanwhile, call him Rem Dogg. It's a two-way street. And no, Leslie, that is not a reference to your chair.

Discipline is a difficult area for Leslie, particularly when Abbey Grove is visited by a VIP. Only Remmy would sidle up to Tom Daley and — at groin-height — ask if Daley's ever 'nursed a chubby in them budgie-smugglers?' Who else asks Peter Mandelson if he 'gets a lot of pussy?' And the recently bankrupt Martine McCutcheon was very surprised by the financial rescue package Leslie offered her. She's got those yoghurt ads, Leslie — McCutcheon's are the healthiest bowels in the business. Knowing that, why would she only charge you £10 a pop?

And on that topic, Leslie, when the next insincere politician asks you what your ambition is, please do not say 'getting my brown wings.' No one over 40 knows what brown wings are, and I'm sick of trying to cover for you. Particularly when I say they're something to do with martial arts, only for you to chip in with 'more like marital arts.' It's clever wordplay, sure. But very, very few women will want to stay married to a man so single-mindedly given over to bottomfoolery.

History:

I'm sad to say that Leslie shows no interest in History. He blames me for this, ever since he found out that Game of Thrones wasn't historically accurate. To be fair to him, we'd been studying series one for the best part of a fortnight before Jing forced me to read the Wikipedia page. What can I say? Like Leslie, I was shocked and saddened. I tried to make it up to the class by setting them my favourite ever essay question:

'Sean Bean's first death was in Caravaggio (1986), in which he plays a young life model who's murdered by the painter Caravaggio. Bean's next notable death comes in Patriot Games (1992), in which he plays an IRA terrorist. In 1995's Goldeneye, Bean's Alec Trevelyan is a sort of mash-up of the two: a homoerotic super-villain who falls onto a satellite. From Boromir's death in Fellowship of the Ring (2001), though, Bean has begun an inexorable decline into being shot dead in a series of feeble straight-to-DVD action films. What does this tell us about the West's post-Cold War socio-political landscape?'

Rem Dogg's answer to this question was short and sweet: 'Caravaggio — ain't that what they call Mitchell's gyppo mum?'

I've only once succeeded in making Leslie take an interest in History since the Game of Thrones disaster. We were discussing how History affects us in our own lives. Leslie thought for a minute, and then explained how you — his parents — had seen his internet history. Apparently, his lively and wide-ranging interest in pornography gave you some cause for concern, and the scandal has left Leslie stuck behind more firewalls than the CIA report on who killed JFK. I can't blame you for being worried.

Boob

Hills

Report Card

Name: Stephen Carmichael

Form behaviour:

Stephen is the Ashley Cole of Form K, if only because we all know he deep-down really loves Cheryl. He's the only non-fat person I've ever met who is genuinely 'bubbly', and I mean that as a compliment. Stephen will always look out for his friends. When Chantelle was ill, Stephen camped alone for Beyoncé tickets in nothing more than a onesie. And not only did he pay for Nadia Pappadopolopokis to have laser hair removal, he paid all over again when Nadia made the mistake of getting her privates lasered instead of her luxuriant moustache. That's the kind of guy Stephen is.

Here's an example of Stephen as Form K's peacemaker. After months of Facebook chat, I'd managed to convince the girl of Joe Poulter's dreams to hook up with the big guy at the Bassingbourn indoor ski centre. But Joe being Joe, he insisted on splitting hairs. No, the girl didn't think she was meeting Joe Poulter per se, and yes, 'I' had 'told' her she'd actually be meeting will.i.am. I told Joe to jibber inconsequential nonsense in a high voice, clapping and weeping at every inspirational thing the woman said. I even offered to lend him my spinny chair (if not the special back cushion I've got on it — a mate's a mate, but my spine's in agony and the thing cost me £40). But this wasn0t good enough for Joe. I nearly punched him.

Where would we have been without Stephen? It was the work of a moment for him to dress Joe in a little bow tie, a single creepy leather driving glove and some 3D glasses he'd stolen from Cineworld. One short message outlining some serious medical problems affecting 'will.i.am' later, and Joe was in business. I hear he sealed the deal 'in the queue for the button lift'. Which sounds like one of Rem Dogg's euphemisms.

Clothing is, unfortunately, the one subject Stephen and I always disagree on. I'll level with you — I'm a flamboyant dresser. I won't hesitate to combine a brown cardigan with my precious white jeans à la Marvin from JLS. Lesser men may not wear a Christmas jumper in April, but I'm not one of them. Hell, if the weather's good, I'll crack open my Birkenstocks. Open-toed sandals with wrap-around arch support? What's not to love?

A lot, according to Stephen. When I wore them with my Christmas jumper, he said I looked like Fred West on holiday, before bursting into tears. But I can't help being ahead of the curve. Sorry, Stephen, you're Coco Chanel with your dull old black dress (read: school uniform). Me? Abbey Grove's Gaultier. I wouldn't look out of place in *Fifth Element*, and I'm proud of that.

In other news, Stephen's recently treated us to his long-awaited one-man version of the late-90s cancer classic *Stepmom*. I don't mind admitting I wept when his Susan Sarandon was diagnosed. Though I was disturbed when he acted out the shower scene with Ed Harris and Julia Roberts. I'm convinced it didn't last that long in the movie.

History:

Stephen takes History very personally. I have had to explain to him that it's not my fault we don't do a module on Princess Diana, but I believe his Twitter campaign has got some positive responses from the ~~tools~~ ~~morons~~ people who set these ludicrous exams.

Report Card

Name: Mitchell Harper

Form behaviour:

If Form K was a film, I would be played by Ben Affleck. We both have lantern jaws. We've also both been made to look like fools by the women we love (in Baffleck's case, J.Lo, in mine, R.Gul) but we've both come out the other side of being total twats better and stronger men.

Mitchell, meanwhile, would be played by Tom Hardy. When I watched *The Dark Knight Rises*, I was struck by the uncanny similarities between Mitchell and Bane: shaved head, military boots and ultra-violent manner, plus that husky voice (for Bane, the result of that weird mask; for Mitchell, the result of all those Rothmans). Bane and Mitchell are so similar, in fact, that I'd have pointed it out to my friend during that midnight showing on the first day of the movie's release, had I not been completely alone.

So he's scary, but Mitchell's got the best banter in class. Like the time I told him 'Don't act like the twat,' and Mitchell replied 'At least I seen a twat. If you had to act like a fanny, it would be about 99% guesswork.' Brilliant. I couldn't help laughing — he's that quick. Jing said the whole episode was a tad misogynistic, but that's women for you.

Mitchell's also raised pranking to an art form. Whether he's putting a whoopee cushion on Joe's seat, selling Fraser some 'magic beans', pouring petrol into Miss Pickwell's worm farm (code name: *Lebensworm*), or filming the PE teacher in a compromising situation, I'm the first to applaud him. However, not long ago one of these pranks resulted in a tragedy. I speak, of course, of my white trousers `à la Marvin from JLS.

Did Mitchell need to smear a thin layer of Nutella on my chair? Stephen may have thanked Mitchell for this, but Chantelle was devastated. Miss Gulliver, meanwhile, thought I had some kind of secret medical problem, and persuaded the school nurse to perform a number of intimate tests on me. When Mitchell's had the latex-glove treatment, maybe he'll understand what I went through that day in the nurse's office. Honestly, the woman's as rough as an American soldier on the Mexican border. The incident affected me badly. All I can say is, I didn't sit down for a week. Which, on second thoughts, was a mistake to say in front of Mitchell.

History:

Mitchell's enthusiasm for violence particularly suits Class Wars. British schoolchildren spend roughly twelve years learning about the Nazis, perhaps because the Second World War is the only war in which we're definitely the 'goodies'. Because of this, I've watched Mitchell fight his way through France, Italy, North Africa and Burma. He takes no prisoners, and his treatment of captured Nazi swine like Joe Poulter can get a tad rough. But those were the realities of war. And I challenge any other teacher to say that they've got Mitchell Harper running towards one of their lessons.

Away from Class Wars, I enjoyed Mitchell's essay on why the 'best' dictators — Hitler, Stalin, Thatcher — have moustaches. For the record, though, Nadia Pappadopolopokis in Form D is not a dictator. Strong-willed, yes, but she's Greek. Say what you like about dictators, but they are organised. The Greeks? Not so much. And forget their economy — those guys can't even do the washing-up without smashing everything up.

However, I didn't enjoy Mitchell trying to grow a moustache. You can't shave in class, something I've had to tell Chantelle. Plus, that shaving loads thing is a myth. All it gives you is fuzzy nipples and a red-raw chest. So I'm told.

Report Card

Name: Jing Hua

Form behaviour:

Jing is a lifesaver in so many ways. She's able to take the register — not as easy as it looks. She's also bothered to learn first aid — again, not as easy as it looks — which means she can do that thing when you jam a biro into someone's throat when they're having trouble breathing. I just wonder if she needs to try doing it to me every time I cough.

I'm joking. I'm always joking. Something Jing could bear in mind when she gets all 'offended' by me slightly misunderstanding her culture. I was surprised that she had three brothers, because I thought the Chinese were like the Royal Family: heir and a spare, then leave it. But I'm really, really glad you guys kept Jing. I can't speak for the third brother. They're always a bit tricky. You know, did the Queen need to keep Prince Edward?

I think of Jing as being Form K's tiger mum. And for all those critics of tiger mums out there, I've got two words: Lang Lang. Actually, that's just one word twice, but you get the point. Jing Jing (as I like to call her) actually taught Rem Dogg how to play 'Twinkle, Twinkle, Little Star' on the keyboard, using only a semi-rigid ruler. His wrists were a bit sore, but at least that put a dampener on Mr. and Mrs. Remmington's Wi-Fi bill for a day or two.

Jing may be intellectually advanced, but in other ways she's still a tween. To illustrate her innocence, here's a story that Jing's begged me not to tell you. She'd lost her crème brûlée of a heart (a rock-hard exterior guarding an inner, custardy sweetness) to a boy called Philip. Now, I personally thought this Philip character was punching way above his weight. Jing's like those women in mid-90s romcoms: when she takes off her glasses and shakes out her hair, your teenage daughter is a fox. At least a 7.5. An 8 on days she's not angry. But this Philip was your classic dweeb. Maths, library, yawn. He even played chess — not the cool chess I do, human chess, but shit chess in a little room with another dweeb. But love is love, and Jing was in it like a pig in ~~shit~~ love.

The problem was, Philip was an aloof little bugger. Jing had tried to catch his eye in Maths by toying with a protractor, coquettishly solving Pythagorean equations etc, but no joy. I maintain typing '5318008' upside down on Philip's calculator would've done the job, but whatever. But then Chantelle stepped in. Usually, it's Jing giving Chantelle advice on homework, exams and the legal ramifications of being charged with a restraining order. But that day, Jing became the pupil, Chantelle the sensei, and her message was one of the wisest, most deeply human things I've ever heard:

'Babe, go talk to him but don't make eye contact, because that can scare shy guys. Laugh a lot, flutter your eyelashes, remember your posture — boobs up but not out. Loosen your hair, take off your glasses; rest your hand on his arm for just that little bit too long. Only then do you look him deep and long in the eye and offer to toss him off after Physics.'

And I'm happy to say Jing followed these instructions to the letter!

History:

This is where Jing and I come to blows (not literally — that was a rumour — but, for the record, I would definitely beat her in a fight, no matter what everyone else says). She's a fact guy. Me? I freewheel. Yes, Braveheart, U-571 or Avatar aren't entirely 'accurate', but how am I going to teach my lot if I can't show them videos? I'm not a bloody miracle-worker. Jesus, Jing, get off my back.

Report Card

Name: Joe Poulter

Form behaviour:

To quote Andrew Lloyd-Webber, how do you solve a problem like Joe? I'm always trying to bring him out of his big shell. Like this one time, I made him dress in a white tuxedo and sing 'Sexual Healing' to Miss Gulliver. This went down really well — the whole canteen was laughing. Remember, Joe, laugh and the world laughs with you, cry and you'll cry alone. I've always lived by that motto, even when Atticus Hoye put his hands down my dungarees at Guy Thompson's birthday barn dance. I was laughing my head off.

I'm the cheery clowning Robin Williams to Joe's kid with leukaemia (Patch Adams), kid who ages normally (Jack), or ghettoised Jew (Jakob the Liar, the thinking man's Schindler's List). But am I thanked for my friendship? No. That's because Joe remains essentially a buzz-kill. He'll call me exploitative, manipulative, mendacious and a lot of other long, mean words from the past. Well, I don't have nicknames for you, butt-munch, so who's more mature?

Don't let his doughty frame fool you — Joe can be a little bitch sometimes. I am still under official investigation as the result of one little Poulter prank. Yes, I made an exorcist cast the devil out of an eleven-year-old. But look at it from my perspective: if you're a mum and you give birth to an albino, don't call him Casper. And what was I going to do when my 'pal' Joe bursts in saying he's seen a ghost, the dick?

But I'm a loyal guy. The other kids may call Joe 'chicken dipper', but that's wrong on many levels. If anything, Joe is sometimes a little bit of a chicken kiev — flaky on the outside, hollow and acrid on the inside. Not that I'd tell him that, because I'm his friend.

And yes, Joe, will.i.am debacle aside, I am your friend. Possibly your only friend. I'm certainly the only friend who regularly goes to the arcade with you to play Time Crisis. House of the Living Dead is a hundred times better, but if you're afraid of zombies and can't get to grips with a plastic shotgun, who am I to judge? Time Crisis it is. Just don't expect me to wipe your bottom in the event of a zombie apocalypse.

I'm the only friend, moreover, who will accompany him to the kebab shop, buy him tickets to 18s and hold his hand around the scary parts (does that sound weird, or is it me?). I'm the only friend who'll willingly file false reports against those pupils who bully Joe (and me), leading to three suspensions and one expulsion. I'm certainly the only friend who's ever taken him to a strip club. Joe complained that I only took him because I'd told Svetlana I was also a single parent bringing up a 'slow' child. But all Joe had to do was keep his mouth shut and his bib on. Was that so tricky? Little Vladimir managed it.

Sure, I ask him for one or two small favours. But Joe should stop being so hostile. After all, isn't it obvious that I'm his number-one fan? Chicken kievs are delicious, the ideal meal for one. I should know — I eat alone most nights. And obviously I understand Joe's insecurities. In many ways, we're the same person. We're the only two people I know, for instance, who enjoyed *Meet the Little Fockers*. Yeah, we're freaks, but we're in it together, all the way.

Joe, mate, you've got to believe in yourself.

History:

C minus. Really woeful.

Boobs

Miss I. Pickwell
Deputy Head Teacher

Mitchell Harper and his associate 'Rem Dogg' recently burst into my office to find me feeding my pet snake. Not with my own milk, I hasten to add. I tried that, but the animal gnawed at the teat somewhat. Having abandoned breastfeeding, I decided to feed mice to Gideon. And, yes, I have named the snake after our current Chancellor of the Exchequer.

Gideon's a greedy little fellow; he devours rodents as though they were heavily mortgaged members of the working class. I'm so happy watching another worthless creature slowly dissolve in Gideon's belly that I sometimes even forget that the Iron Lady has gone to smash the Angels' Union in Heaven.

Anyway, Harper and 'Rem Dogg' entered my office under the illusion that I was still in the showers, conducting my fortnightly hygiene check on the girls' netball team. They were carrying spray cans of paint, a bucketful of mince and a box of matches. God knows what they were planning, but quite the fright they had to find me spoon-feeding Gideon the business end of Minnie Mouse.

It turns out that the boys find my serpentine predilections – quote – 'F***ing weird, Miss man.' Harper even had the cheek to compare me to Voldemort, as though the Dark Lord had anything like my wicked charisma. Naturally, I put the pair of them in detention for a week.

To get their own back, Harper and 'Dogg' conducted some stealthy raids to cut off Gideon's food at the source, namely the caretaker's deep freeze. The caretaker doesn't have a snake of his own, so it's not entirely clear why he has a deep freeze full of mice. He did once refer to their frozen tails as lollipop sticks, but I assume this was in jest.

I was scouring Harper's bag for mice, therefore, when I came across this. It's a thoroughly unprofessional document, designed by Mr. Wickers to embezzle funds and assets from the government. I assume you'll sack him the moment you've read it, so I won't bother chasing down the caretaker for more mice. Once he's no longer required by Abbey Grove, Wickers will prove a delicious treat for Gideon.

What follows clearly represents an idiot's view of dyslexia.

HOW TO GET A LAPTOP OFF
THE GOVERNMENT

By Alfie 'Artful Dodger' Wickers

Drawings by Stephen 'Craig David' Carmichael

Re-e-wind, this goes out to Form K. Now, I know you've all been banned from the IT rooms since the webcam episode. And on the topic, can I just say that I was the only teacher who didn't crack like a small-time bitch under narco interrogation, yo.

Yeah, all the parents were like, 'Abbey Grove doesn't need its own Babe Station.' But I pointed out that everyone needs to make a few Gs, plus you guys were the perfect team: Chantelle's the babe, Stephen's costume and make-up, Jing does the tech shit, Mitchell and Rem Dogg collect the debts, and Joe... Joe's probably the kind of sap who'd give us his card deets just so Chantelle moves her hand a little bit. Flawless. That said, I'm glad no one knows I fronted the cash for the website, because the grown-ups are all pretty pissed.

That's the thing about teachers. They're never bloody happy. One minute they're banning you lot from IT (like it's Oceana or something), the next they're complaining that you haven't done your homework. I've explained that you guys need computers to work, but Pickwell won't lift the ban. So this is what we're going to do.

A history lesson. Dyslexia was invented in 1996 by an individual known as Parent Zero. Parent Zero held a dinner party for some other middle-class parents, who were all boasting about their amazing, super-talented children. Hearing about these little Mozarts, Shakespeares and Rooneys, Parent Zero felt her heart sink at the thought of her perfectly normal son's ever-so-slightly below-average exam results.

'How's little Tarquin doing?' another mother asked. How could Parent Zero escape the ignominy of having a fairly average son? Then, in a stroke of genius, she decided that her child had a problem...

'Oh, Tarquin is such an intelligent boy,' she said. 'But he hasn't designed a spaceship for NASA or won the Nobel Prize just yet, because of his terrible illness.'

The parents gasped, feigning sympathy. 'What illness?' they asked. Parent Zero searched for a word.

'Dys...lex...ia,' she said. And so the myth was born.

Now, Joe may disagree with my version of events. He may use things like 'science' and 'facts' to prove that dyslexia is real. He may even claim that I'm dylsexix ymsel. Jing might also call me 'a clueless, madman.' And maybe I am completely and utterly wrong to abuse the system in this way. Fine. Dyslexia could actually be a real thing. But the government is still giving out free laptops to people willing to play the game. Obviously laptops aren't cheap, so the local authorities try to weed out any chancers. But their tests – though rigorous – are easy enough to cheat if you follow my top tips for rinsing the government.

Top Tips

1. Most rookies think tricking a suit into believing you're dyslexic is simple. 'Just write with your left hand during the aptitude test,' they'll say, 'and the iMac is yours.' Well, they couldn't be more wrong. Shitty handwriting is page-one stuff: a good start, but don't rely on it to seal the deal. It may get you eighteen hours of extra time for each GCSE, but will it guarantee you a laptop? Dream on.

2. The expert 'dyslexic' will start their campaign weeks in advance, with their letter to the local authorities requesting a dyslexia test. Do not send an email! Remember, you have no access to IT, which is why you need a laptop. It's incredible how many people fall at this first hurdle.

3. Your letter should be an unpunctuated, badly spelt mess, written in crayon on the back of a brochure for adult literacy classes. This letter should have been sent to at least three wrong addresses before it gets to the relevant person. It should also have either too many stamps or too few stamps – either way, it shows them that you've misread the numbers on the Post Office's weighing scales. If you learn one thing from me, guys, it's that success is built on details.

4. Miss your first test. This may sound foolhardy but, if you can't handle high stakes, then this ain't your game. Think of the dyslexia test as being like *Die Hard*. People from the local authorities are like the cold, efficient villain, Hans Gruber. You are John McClane, outmanned and outgunned by 20:1. What's McClane's only advantage? A little bit of crazy. The Grubers running the test will expect you to show up, punctually and with your own stationery, at the time they've assigned you. But would a real dyslexic do such a thing (if, of course, dyslexia was real in the first place)? No way. So get tough, play dirty, and exploit the element of surprise. Drop a crudely built bomb down the Grubers' lift shaft or kill one of them and write 'Ho ho ho' on their T-shirt. Let's see how the bastards deal with that!

5. Mitchell, just to be clear, I was talking in metaphors. Don't kill anyone.

6. When the authorities organize a second test for you, camp outside their offices the night before. Big, slightly 'special' gestures work magic on your average dyslexia tester. Tell them you camped because you can't even read a watch (let alone the instructions to an alarm clock), and the battle's pretty much over before it's begun.

7. Clothing: on test day, wear a helmet. They always set alarm bells ringing. Preferably also wear a comedy T-shirt, but don't worry if this is taking things too far. Only world-class bell-ends like Fraser wear comedy T-shirts, so I appreciate that – while you want an iMac – you may also want your dignity. Everyone has their price; I wouldn't wear an 'iPorn' T-shirt to save my mother's life.

8.Stephen's wardrobe for the 'dyslexic' is spot-on, apart from picking on my orthopedic shoes. You might not have weak bridges and webbed toes, Stephen, but I'd thank you not to laugh at my very serious disabilities.

9.When you are handed your test paper, eat it. In the good old days, you could get away with just circling the same letter on all the multiple-choice questions. But this is austerity Britain and laptops don't come cheap – you need to knock this shit out the park, whatever the cost to your bowels.

10.When they let you do the test on a computer, nail it, then pretend like you've never seen one of these life-changing magic machines before. The penny will drop.

Finally, remember actually 'being' dyslexic is no help whatsoever. Joe's failed the dyslexia test three times. I, on the other hand, did so well faking the illness that they gave me two laptops – one for me, and one for my new carer. How's that for artful dodging?

WORK EXPERIENCE

Mitchell Harper

Teachers Name:	Mr Dickers		**Class:** 5K	**Date:**	06.05

Duration & Location:	4 weeks in a hospital
Curriculum Area and VELS:	Biology
Teaching Focus:	Drugs testing
Objectives:	Drugs testing
Resources:	Drugs

Pupil Feedback

My work experience was having drugs tested on me in hospitals. It was a crap job for a number of reasons. First off, right, I thought they were gonna be proper drugs. Gurning my tits off for money? Sign me up! I always thought my dad running his own funfair was the best job in the world, but this drugs thing sounded sick. I told Dickers and the others about my great gig.

'Chemical testing?' Dickers asked. 'What, are the L'Oréal labs missing a monkey?' He's so childish.

'Yeah, cos that monkey's too busy shagging your mum,' I replied in a flash of what Fraser calls my Wildean wit.

'Yeah, after he's shagged your mum,' Wickers stuttered.

'When's he found the time to shag my mum when he's not finished shagging your dad yet?' Chicken Zinger!

'Can you stop talking about monkeys and start teaching us about the Battle of El-Alamein?' Jing interrupted. She was seriously pissy that morning, ever since Dickers compared Chinese children to the shoe-making elves in some bent myth about cobblers.

'I don't get why everyone tries to stop puppies having lipstick and perfume put on them,' Stephen interrupted. 'I believe every animal deserves to look fabulous.'

'Babe, are you doing your impression of Nicole Scherzwinger again?' Chantelle asked, not sure if Stephen meant to sound that thick.

'Anyway, Mitchell, why would anyone pay a sixteen-year-old to take meow-meow?' Jing asked me. At the time, I blamed Dickers for making her so cynical about my new job.

'I dunno. Meow-meow's just a fertiliser — maybe B&Q were doing some market research?' I replied.

And it's about time they did, cos me and Rem Dogg go round the B&Q most weekends eating random shit looking for a new legal high, and our own 'research' has been pretty disappointing. Rem got the shits off some wood-chippings and I got banned when security caught me licking a trowel.

Annoyingly, it turns out Jing was right. I was being trialled on for medical drugs — pills for hay fever, indigestion, headaches and stuff. I just sat in a room feeling giddy for a month. Plus, no one wants to buy any of the shit I stole from the labs. You can't deal in prototype Rennies, even to a twat like Joe Poulter. This was gutting, cos I'd been banking on turning a profit to pay off a couple of overdue instalments on my PS3.

It was definitely the worst work experience I heard about. Even Frank Grayson had a better time. He went to work for a tabloid newspaper and he had a wicked time. As the office bitch, Frank used to type up messages off of celebrities' answer-phones. Apparently, all the A-listers spend their time not returning Sienna Miller's calls. None of them seem to want to reminisce about Glasto 2006.

As for me, I'm going back to the fair. Dad says if I work hard enough, one day I'll be able to stop bending air rifles' barrels at the shooting stalls and become that guy who gets to stand up on a bumper car in between goes. I'm working on a dream, people.

WORK EXPERIENCE

Jing Chow

Teachers Name:	Mr. Wickers	Class:	5K	Date:	01.05
Duration & Location:	2 weeks/Abbey Grove School				
Curriculum Area and VELS:	All subjects will be covered				
Teaching Focus:	Tutoring Mr. Wickers				
Objectives:	Tutoring Mr. Wickers				
Resources:	Me				

Pupil Feedback:

On the last day of term, Mr. Wickers sidled up to me and asked what I planned to do for work experience. I told him I was shadowing our local MP, as I've always wanted to get into politics.

Mr. Wickers snorted, then told me that getting into politics was 'a piece of piss'. He boasted of his time as a student activist: at one point, he'd chained himself to the railings outside Parliament in protest at Hertfordshire Uni's firewall on its internet server. His campaign – 'Child Lock: Throw Away The Key' – had succeeded in raising public awareness of freedom of information. A photo of Mr. Wickers had even appeared in the press, albeit the *Watford Observer*. Unfortunately, the photo appeared under the headline 'Students Are Wankers', thanks to the ulterior motives of his fellow 'comrade dissidents'.

There were only two of these comrades, a pair of sweaty youths in leather trench-coats called Cecil Stinchcombe and Billy Probert. But they were enough to skew the public's perception of the *Child Lock* campaign. Mr. Wickers wanted to free up students' access to an 'adult' historical role-play site, War Wench. He claims this aim was purely academic, but that Stinchcombe and Cave piggy-backed 'the movement' to demand the more universal right to pleasure themselves on university property.

Mr. Wickers maintains that he'd set out to start a Wikileaks revolution in Hertfordshire. But the fact that Stinchcombe and Cave are separately under caution for acts of gross indecency brings into disrepute the 'non-sexual, non-creepy' motivations of the self-styled Watford Assange. Having said that, Mr. Wickers did receive a letter of support from Silvio Berlusconi, so (he claims) 'it wasn't a total waste of time.'

When I told him my political aspirations were of a slightly greater magnitude, Mr. Wickers told me to throw myself under the King's horse because 'that's worked for birds in the past'.

'By birds,' I replied, 'do you mean the militant suffragette Emily Davidson, who died at the Epsom Derby on the 4th June 1913, and whose motives for stepping in front of George V's horse remain unclear? And, if so, then I think you're being reductive, sexist and patronising.'

'Women?' Mr. Wickers replied, ruffling my hair. He finds it hysterical to be 'un-PC' when teaching us how women got the vote – by the end of the Modern Democracy module, he'd taken to wearing shapeless, high-waisted jeans and a tragic leather jacket.

'How did women's lib go from nought to sixty in just thirty-odd years?' he says, in his best Jeremy Clarkson voice. This sounds like the nodding bulldog in the Churchill ads, if the dog came from the South, took massive amounts of cocaine, and was a misogynist (perhaps due to a professional rivalry with those women in the Diamond car insurance ad?). 'Captain Slow?'

He calls me Captain Slow in these lessons. I try to answer his ludicrous questions sensibly as 'Clarkson' paces around the classroom, which has been rearranged so that the class are all standing in a circle around him. 'Clarkson' also makes Rem Dogg wear a white boiler suit and helmet. I assume this is another reference to Top Gear – I don't watch it myself, because I have a brain.

Pupil Feedback (cont):

But back to the last day of term. To Mr. Wickers' suggestion that I throw myself in front of the King's horse, I replied that this might be tricky, given that we don't currently have a King. But Mr. Wickers persisted, advising me to 'smear myself in Pedigree Chum and get savaged by some Corgis.' He promised to buy me all the dog food I needed if I'd do him this one, small favour...

Then Mr. Wickers confessed that he wasn't a qualified teacher. I have been telling him this for months, but it turns out that it is literally true. Mr. Wickers was 'training on the job', aiming to complete his QTS (Qualified Teacher Status) in the forthcoming holidays. Mr. Fraser had let him teach at Abbey Grove because Mr. Wickers promised to play maracas in his rap-folk fusion 'massive' Mumford and N***as, a name of which Mr. Wickers is rightly ashamed.

After this admission, the rest of the pathetic tale tumbled out. Mr. Wickers had failed the qualification exams twice. If he failed a third time, he would be sacked. He begged me to tutor him – this was his last chance. Though it was pleasant to imagine being taught by a proper teacher, my peculiar loyalty to Mr. Wickers (perhaps the only wholly inexplicable phenomenon in the known universe) won me round. I'm a thrill-seeker, living for the next academic buzz; educating a chump like Wickers might be the *ultimate* challenge. And so my addict's logic led me into the most trying month of my life.

He may be an unconventional teacher, but Mr. Wickers' professional incompetence is dwarfed by his woeful inability as a student. I see now why he's so matey with Rem Dogg – they are genuinely on an academic par. Actually, Rem may be better than Mr. Wickers at science. And maths. And French, even though Rem Dogg's French vocab comes exclusively from the extremely violent movie, La Haine ('so good you kinda forget it's in black and

Pupil Feedback (cont):

white'). He's never yet managed to complete a French oral exam, having driven a succession of teachers to tears with his threatening 'Frog banter'.

I soon realized that 'teaching' Mr. Wickers would be pointless. But politics is the art of pragmatism, so I decided to work with what I'd got. And what *did* I have? No more than the rude tool of a bearded slacker with a fox's cunning and an Oxfam pair of cords. It was for this reason, then, that Mr. Wickers and I devised the most thorough system of cheating since Lance Armstrong started oxidising his blood.

To give credit where credit's due, Mr. Wickers committed to defrauding educational standards with a conviction he never brought to study. He even got a few small tattoos of historical dates and teaching buzzwords, tattoos that might raise eyebrows if ever he finally sleeps with someone.

On the day of the exam, I dressed as a cleaner and infiltrated the exam facility. Thus disguised, I was able to hide laminated answer sheets in the cistern of the men's loo. After a few scheduled toilet breaks and some furtive glances at the tattoos on his inner thigh (the Oxfam cords have a torn gusset), Mr. Wickers passed his exam.

Like the lab technician who splices his genes with those of an insect, I have created a scientific miracle (i.e. a qualified Alfie Wickers) that may yet turn on its maker and destroy me. But a pyrrhic victory is a victory nonetheless. I am haunted by guilt, but that can't obliterate the pride I take in having achieved the impossible. They said it couldn't be done. Well, I did it on work experience. May God have mercy on my soul.

WORK EXPERIENCE

Joe Poulter

Teachers Name:	Mr Wickers		Class:	6K		Date:	01.06

Duration & Location: 1 week and my Dad's massage parlour

Curriculum Area and VELS: None really

Teaching Focus: Massaging blokes

Objectives: Getting out of having to massage blokes

Resources: Baby oil

Pupil Feedback:

My dad used to be a regional manager in Woolworths, making me I the golden-haired prince of pick-n-mix counters stretching from Welwyn to Tring. I'd never leave a Woolies without one pocket of gummy bears, another of little fried eggs and a plaited necklace of strawberry shoelaces — all for free! I admit the power went to my head (or, rather, my expanding tummy), but Mitchell's suggestion that I was somehow instrumental in Woolworth's bankruptcy is still stupid. It's not like I was shoplifting the toys, apart from one Spiderman costume, once. It didn't fit. Damn you, pick-n-mix.

So I didn't make Woolies go bust, but bust it went, leaving my dad out of a job. Unemployment coincided with a mid-life crisis that had been brewing ever since mum had a brief fling with her trainer at Virgin Active. Mitchell didn't see what my dad was so upset about, as it's very unlikely that I share any DNA with a fitness instructor). But it still took years to shake my father out of his funk. It was only when Woolies shut, in fact, that dad seemed to come to life. The very day he left work, he sat me and mum down and explained that he'd always had a secret desire in him, a burning passion that until now he'd felt unable to talk about, such was the stigma and the shame with which our narrow-minded society burdened men like him.

My mum burst into tears and said she'd always known.

'Always?' my dad said. 'I thought I'd hidden it from you.'

'No, Philip. I saw the way you looked at Mr. Wickers. Well, go to him if you must, but know that you've broken my heart.'

At this point, my dad realised there'd been some wires crossed. No, he explained, he wasn't coming out — and did my mum really think he'd been gay all along? — but confessing to his life-long dream of becoming a masseur.

'A masseur? Like a masseuse?' I ask, very confused.

'You see!' he roared, angrily. 'This is the prejudice I'm talking about. My own son! Masseur is masculine, masseuse is feminine. The words are not interchangeable. I am still a red-blooded man...' and here his voice broke, 'with feelings.'

So dad used his redundancy money to retrain as a masseur, then got a massive loan from the bank to open a massage parlour in Oring. He'd clearly learnt nothing from the credit crunch — his loan was back-breaking, and he's recently been forced to make his two co-workers redundant. So for my work experience, I decided to help him out at the parlour.

I'd never seen my dad masseuring before, but Mitchell's jokes about happy endings had struck a nerve. So, on the first day, I did have slight misgivings about my dad pottering around in a white, unisex trouser suit, putting on a whale-song CD then squeezing a tube of lube into his hands. But he loves his job so much that I soon came to think of him kneading another man's inside thigh as just another day in the office. After all, who was I to judge? My dad does the job he loves. He helps people recover from injuries, discomfort and depression. I'm proud of him. As massage is his gift to the world. That said, when he offered me a go on that guy's thighs, I ran a bloody mile.

WORK EXPERIENCE

Teachers Name: Mr Wickers	Class: 5K	Date: 01.05

Duration & Location: 2 months at fit birds' houses

Curriculum Area and VELS: Getting some action

Teaching Focus: Getting some action

Objectives: Getting some action

Resources: My tools

Pupil Feedback:

This holidays, I became a plumber. Mitchell told me that was stupid cos most toilets were on the first floor, but I've never been afraid to be ambitious. I'd done some research, you see, on some adult websites, and plumbers get bare pussy. Well, either plumbers or the guys who clean swimming pools, but there was two problems with me being one of them: there ain't many pools in Tring, and I ain't good round deep water.

So plumbing it was. As I say, I'd researched it loads online, so I thought I knew what was in store for me. But never in my wildest dreams did I think I was gonna get so much action!

My first job was fixing a leaky u-bend. I had my buckets and plumbing clobber with me, but they all fell from my hands when the door opened to reveal the u-bender's worried owner. She was well fit with massive tits and long hair and legs and everything, man. I made a pretence of checking the rivets on the u-bend, but then she started leaning over me so her tits were on my head like a sexy hat, innit. So we started banging for six hours solid. She said I had the biggest penis she ever seen. But then suddenly we heard the front door slam and she was like, 'Oh God, it's my other half!'

I panicked, cos I didn't want some big bloke to catch me doing his wife up in the tradesman's way, if you get me. But then the 'other half' walked in and it was a she! Yeah, another bird, and she didn't seem too upset. Turns out the first yat said 'Oh God!' only cos she didn't want to share me with the second yat. We had a threesome and they spent loads of time kissing each other's barookas.

'I'm glad I met you benders,' I joked really funnily. The girl both laughed for ages, then the second woman also said that I had the biggest penis she ever seen. They'd wore themselves out about midnight, finally shattered after I'd given them wave upon wave of orgasms, each bigger and more all-consuming than the last. As I picked up all my buckets and plumber stuff, they were like, 'Rem Dogg, you are the most amazing lover ever. Stay with us and let's have sex all day for the rest of the holidays.'

'Nah, I'm gonna play the field like Mark Wright,' I replied, leaving them with nothing more than many, many memories for the wank bank, a bit of a limp, and a leaking u-bend.

And so it went for like two months. Every day I'd end up having three-, four- or fivesomes with a load of fit women with big boobs and nice bums who all said I'd got the biggest penis they'd ever seen. I was making loads of money, too, because the women were paying me to do overtime. Then the holidays was over, which was well sad, because I liked all the shagging. We had a big farewell orgy, me and like a hundred birds, yeah, and I'm gonna miss the wild excess. Oh well, I guess deep down I'm a one-woman guy...

Mitchell's mum, daddy's back and he's learnt a whole load of new tricks!

Franimals

Pizza Tycoon was made twenty years ago, i.e. older than every single pupil here apart from Frank Grayson (he-llooo four years of failing to even sit your GCSEs, let alone pass them). But it never gets old. I can't turn on my computer without having a go at designing my perfect pizza – anchovies for brine, gorgonzola for musk, bacon to seal the deal and pear as the sweet kiss good night, fact-fans. Some say playing computer games at work is unprofessional. I say that this is a special case, because a school is like a pizza. The hard, unyielding crust (Pickwell) rims the ingredients in the middle (everyone else), making sure all these different flavours keep their structure. And at the centre of this pizza? A fried egg going by the name of Shaquille B. Fraser, like a yolky spider at the heart of his delicious web. School Tycoon? I've completed it.

Anyway, this Tokyo Sin malarkey sounds like a different ball game. So different, in fact, that it isn't even using balls any more. Yeah, this ting gone LiLo. I conducted a brief survey into the content of the game

Word. F to the R to the A to the S to the E to the R here. Now, I've heard it through the grapevine that a number of you little tykes have gone cray for a certain video game. I refer, of course, to SS: Dead Light District, in which ninjas kill Nazi prostitutes. A strange premise for 'fun', but then I'm not completely up to 'scr-scr-scratch randmaster Flash' with computer games. I'm no geriatric – I still love shooting the rats on Theme Hospital but, for this Street Fighter, gaming began and ended with Pizza Tycoon.

and the results are disturbing. Rem Dogg assures me that 'Eagle's Nest brothel level is the shit, mate', largely because you can triple Blitz-Kick gargantuanly-bosomed far-right sex workers in the Germanic opulence of Hitler's country retreat. Mitchell favours hunting down fugitive fascists in Argentina, using stealthy nunchucks to drag them to a kangaroo Yakuza court in downtown Tokyo. And Miss Pickwell's favourite level is when you get to go undercover as a Nazi prostitute. She sho' got the tekkers for that. Watching her hump Hermann Goering on a Nintendo Wii was the most disturbing thing I've ever seen in my life, and I've been to the PE teacher's house.

Full disclosure: grandpa don't 'get' Tokyo Sin. Usually, that doesn't cloud my judgement viz crazes. For every craze I love (wheelie shoes, Dragonball poses, conkers, poppers) there'll be another craze I don't, but which I permit nonetheless. Hey, I don't like Spanish, but I still let that BS go down. If you're wondering why I don't like Spanish, BTW, it's a long story involving a Honduran jail. Let's just say that I've learnt to my cost that you address your prison husband with the more formal usted pronoun.

But you've got to admit, you guys are getting a little carried away with Tokyo Sin. Pupil-on-pupil brutality is skyrocketing. Mitchell's wearing a ninja mask, Joe's doing gusset-splitting karate kicks, Stephen broke Grayson's nose (who saw that coming?) and Chantelle's dressed like a hooker, although I don't know if that last one's a coincidence or not. The madness has got to stop.

How do you stop a craze? By replacing it with another craze. And that's maths. So how do I stop you from turning the Abbey Grove playground into an ultra-violent dead light district? Well, I've designed a fairly fruity fad to wean you off Nazi.

'But what is this FFF?' you ask. 'It sure is F-heavy, like your smooth loving.'

'I'm glad you're not a pupil,' I reply, blushing, 'otherwise that compliment could have sounded inappropriate, even if entirely accurate.'

'But I'm not a pupil,' you say, just to be clear. 'Though I am curious about this new craze.'

'Well, anonymous person I'm talking to in my head, I give you... Franimals. They're pun-derful (wonderful) fun!'

Yup, animals made out of fruit. Make 'em, swap 'em, eat 'em. Maybe even unleash your inner Frankenstein and mate 'em,

tampering with the very fabric of the franimal kingdom to breed new and strange mutant life forms beyond their creators' control. Though there are quite a number of breeds to play with already! They are:

Appleotomus

Appleotomus – or pomme d'mud if you will (a clever French pun. French, I likey. I've never been in a Parisian prison). This slow-moving titan of the franimal kingdom can be found bathing in the brown waters of the Limpopo River, which I've made using chocolate milk and Tupperware I've decorated with ferns. Eat yourself out, David Attenborough!

Crocoavocadile

The dark green scaly skin of an avocado is very reptilian, making the avocado (which is a fruit) the perfect building block from which to craft a crocoavocadile. As befitting one of the top rungs on the franimal food chain, the crocoavocadile lurks around the lapping shores of the Limpopo, gobbling up pretty much anything. Again, the avocado is perfect for this; once de-stoned, there is a cavity within the croc big enough for a chunk of appleotomus, a baby orangeutan (made from a satsuma or, if half-digested, some segments of a clementine) or a Lego man.

Orangeutan

I've always been scared of orangutans; their receding ginger hairline, pursed mouths and black, bulging eyes remind me of Anne Robinson, who was very curt to me the one time we met. I'd entered The Weakest Link, but came a cropper on some very open-ended questions.

'What is Scientology?' How can you answer that without sounding libellous? Because – whatever it is – it's not a flipping religion! And I say that as a practising Jedi.

begins! Why not stick a grApe stalk at ninety degrees into a small pot of earth? With the fruit still attached to it, this stalk becomes a tree swarming with our closest relations in the franimal kingdom!

For a particularly hellish Planet of the Apes-style vision, you can even disguise the stalk as the Empire State Building. The trick of perspective makes it look like it's being scaled by an army of lovesick King Kongs. Then you can pretend to be the Air Force shooting them down, popping them one by one between your fingers. Let's see Tokyo Sin rival that for visceral thrills!

Papayhyena

This beauty is crafted from a mangy papaya. Why not add a slavering, razor-toothed maw made from two of the metal cutting bits you get on sellotape dispensers? For veracity, I like to put a couple of papayhyenas around the slit-open belly of a wounded zebranana. When these desert dogs start gorging on the corpses of other franimals, I can 'carrion' having fun for hours!

GrApes

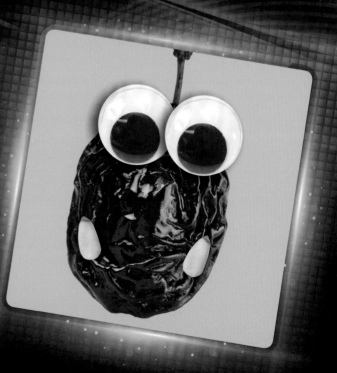

Ingredients: 1 x red grapes, 10 days past their sell-by date. Aged sufficiently, grapes become dark enough to look like apes. Then the fun

Be warned, though - if any of you kids have secretaries, they tend to get quite scared by the noises the eager Franimist makes when he's an airman capping grApes' asses. Turns out a mixture of biplane engine and exploding fruit-simian sounds uncannily like a sex attack. This is not helped by shouting 'grApe' through a fairly solid door, as the 'g' kinda gets lost.

Grizzly Pears

Grizzly Pears - I make these from pears, dipped in PVA glue then rolled in clippings of my own hair. If you're blonde, maybe ask a brunette friend for a donation, or - if you're above Year 3 - look elsewhere for your supply. Nudge, nudge.

I've posed my grizzly pears in a bucolic woodland, made from loo rolls and a patch of Astro Turf stolen from the sports centre. The grizzlies are tearing down a little tent (really the case of a mini kite), the better to savage its Lego man occupant. In his Dr. Doolittle hubris, this Lego naturist had tried to befriend the grizzlies' cubs, played by unripe, partially shaved kiwis. Thus does he learn that the franimal kingdom does not brook the foolishness of man. For extra veracity, use a small amount of spaghetti hoops and ketchup to simulate the Lego man's exposed intestinal tract.

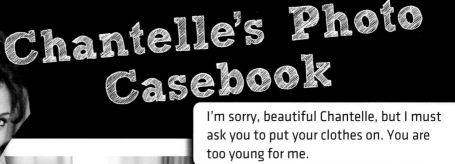

Chantelle's Photo Casebook

NEXT DAY
Fit pool, babes.
Thanks. I am like Katie Price, an astute businesswoman of impeccable taste.
I know. And re Mr. Wickers – you could make Miss Gulliver really angry with him, so that she never wants to see him again. That might free him from her spell.
Mmm, that gives me an idea . . .

LATER
It's getting hot in here . . .

LATER
Alfie was so irresponsible to elope with Chantelle to France. I never want to see him again.
No! Rosie has broken my heart!
But I'm here to sweep up the pieces, sir.
NEXT DAY
Oh, Chantelle, now I see you're way fitter and younger than Gulliver.
Thank you, sir.
Call me Alfie. Actually, we'd better assume new identities as I imagine Interpol will be pretty keen to arrest us. So call me Alfredo.
#bonnieandclyde, Alfredo.
Chantelle, I'm sure you put a lot of work into this, but your homework was an essay on how salt levels affect osmosis. Is sexual obsession a metaphor for a potato becoming rigid in salt solution? I don't get it. Also,

Fraser's Film Pitch

Lego To Get Outta Here

The first shot: a group of international terrorists in a Zipvan. The Zipvan shows that they mean business. Thrifty, minimal paper trail, with no MOT to tie these mothers down. In, out. They'll return the Zipvan to a designated drop-off point with a replenished tank of gas and just walk away, after signing the necessary forms and comparing any new scratches on the van's body work with some digital photographs they'd prudently taken on receipt of the vehicle that morning.

In the van, it's your classic cocktail of henchmen: three parts mad-eyed Arab, two parts German sadomasochist, salty banter round the rim of the glass, and one mirthless Chinaman as the taciturn glacé cherry at the bottom.

(Note: never have more than one Chinese-speaker in any group of terrorists. Kung-fu villains are lone wolves who speak with their fists. Cantonese nattering spoils the air of Eastern mystery as quickly as one of Mitchell Harper's botty coughs.)

They are listening to Chris Brown. Their rental van, their rules.

(Another note: modern action films like to throw in a supermodel villainess into the mix, perhaps making her fight an equally hot FBI agent clad in a cat suit.

But *Lego To Get Outta Here* is the unashamed work of a purist. As I tell Mr. Wickers, forget the *chicas*, *hombre*, this steam room's men-only. Anyway, I doubt many women would want to join in, given that these terrorists are listening to Chris Brown.)

The Zipvan is transporting fifty tonnes of nerve gas from Heathrow to Ascot. The terrorists' plan? To release said nerve gas at the races – thus killing the Queen, a lot of public-school boys, some Irish, cloth-capped bookies, tarts in hats, and approximately thirty horses. (As, I believe, Master Harper's toxic bum-brew could do – lay off the Lucozade and cigarettes, Mitchell, for all our sakes.)

Obviously, the wholesale slaughter of Ascot would only be good for the makers of lasagne ready-meals. Horse meat, not human meat. (Though, to be honest, nothing about Tesco's – or Abbey Grove's canteen – surprises me any more.)

So anyway, an elite unit of counter-terrorist soldiers have been dispatched to intercept the package. They drive a big black van – their own, not a rental. (These guys do shizzle by the book.)

The soldiers are made up of another classic cocktail: five parts featureless grunt, one part new-husband/soon-to-be-dad (the first to die), one part closet psychopath (he's 'seen things'), one part fatally naive captain, one part unsuspecting hero. Let's call this hero Fraquille Shaser. As of yet, we know little of Shaser, beyond him being a strong, brooding presence. The soldiers know they've got no time to waste, particularly after their stop-

off at Heston Blumenthal's Little Chef. Breakfast being the most important meal of the day, they'd set off extra early, coming off the M25 around Chertsey to cruise the pre-rush hour A3 down past Basingstoke ('Amazingstoke' – I was born there) to Heston's Popham-based sausage carnival. Unfortunately for these meticulous planners, the service at Little Chef's was slow. Not appalling, but absent-minded. As a result, the race is on.

The captain wants Shaser to stay on the M3 until it intersects with the M25, circulating clockwise to join the M4 westbound for Slough. But Shaser knows there just isn't time. He also knows that those Olympic Breakfasts are ticking time bombs – they will need to get to facilities fast.

Shaser takes a maverick short cut through Bracknell, intercepting the terrorists around junction 6 of the M4. The terrorists are shameless in their use of fellow motorway users as collateral damage. They shoot up school buses, ambulances and gaily painted minivans for the gifted so that they spin off into the path of the on coming soldiers, like barrels thrown at Donkey Kong.

To put an end to this, Shaser crashes directly into the terrorists, and sends both vans through Windsor, vying for supremacy all along the B3022. So far, so good for the terrorists – Ascot is only 5.3 miles away. What does it matter if they explode in a ball of flames when they get there? Tesco's will still be a thousand microwave meals the richer.

But this all-male choir of international evil hadn't counted on Fraquille Shaser. Evil's implacable foe, he manages to grind the soldiers' van's bumper under the hindquarters of the Zipvan. The ranting Middle Eastern super-terrorist who runs things in the rental van is taken by surprise. He'd previously believed that messing with a man's rental was tantamount to scratching his face in a fist fight. Just not on. But Shaser don't play by no rules except for two sets of rules:

The first set are HMRC's tax regulations. Fraquille's had his fingers burnt. He once tried to claim back *Top Gear* DVDs, on the grounds that they were instructional. Why doesn't top-notch workplace banter qualify as tax deductible? Fraquille will honestly never know.

The second set are his own rules. These are they:

1. Kill terrorists.
2. Have a pun or wisecrack ready for when you kill them. For instance, having pushed a terrorist down an elevator shaft, you want to look down it, wince at the sound of impact and say, 'Next time, take the stairs.'
3. Someday, somehow, and no matter how many casualties it takes ... meet Skrillex.

B3022 ASCOT

Shaser lives by a code. In his eyes, nothing is too dangerous or stupid if his honour is at stake. He does the maths. On his fingers. As he drives. There is only one solution. He double-checks it by doing the maths a second time. He gets a slightly different solution, but the gist of it is clear: stop the terrorists from reaching Ascot.

Bumper to bumper with the Zipvan, Shaser rams it and its deadly cargo through the

paltry perimeter fence that separates the world from that strange and magical place: Legoland.

Stumbling from his upturned van, Shaser quips, 'No oh-*fence*, but next time, use one of the designated entrances.' He wonders if Skrillex is in Legoland. It seems like the kind of place he'd hang out. Then his captain comes and puts his balls in a vice, which he's brought along for the purpose. 'What have you done?' the captain demands. And he's right to be worried.

Let's look at the big picture. Fifty tonnes of nerve gas are now pouring from the totalled Zipvan into Britain's family-orientated, building-block theme park of choice? #clusterfword But this is worse than anyone could ever have imagined.

The nerve gas soon kills off 30 per cent of the terrorists, three-quarters of the meaningless grunts and the new-husband/soon-to-be-dad. (And if those numbers don't make sense, remember that action movies are about passion over numbers, bi-atches.) Eff The Man. Business suit? Don't you mean straitjacket? Necktie? A noose, more like. Follow my lead and wear a clip-on to work. Lemon pastel for choice.

That said, maybe don't follow what Ofsted called my 'under thought and meaningless anti-business rhetoric'. Abbey Grove is crying out for high-achieving graduates. I'm proud of little Davey Isaacs, 17, becoming chief barista at Tring station's Pumpkin Cafe. But it does worry me when we're holding special assemblies to celebrate the fact. Don't get me wrong,

I love a Frap. But:

a) There's more to life than frappuccinos. I'll put my hands up – I'm a big fan of a chai latte.

b) Pumpkin doesn't serve fraps. So what good's that, Davey boy? I'll tell you. Frap all. (FYI: spent all morning on 'frap all'. Underthought? Think not.)

Anyway, some terrorists and a lot of soldiers are dead. Meanwhile, Fraquille Shaser's dark-horse tactics have landed him in the doghouse. Horse-house. Stables. In the stables of poor opinion, Fraquille's newly career-orientated mind takes stock of the situation. (He can take a hint – careers are 'important' all of a sudden, he gets it, whatever. You don't need to start throwing the book at him, Ofsted.)

Taking his balls out of the vice, the naive captain orders Shaser to stand down. The closet psycho is now the captain's right-hand man. And the captain is right-handed. Which means the psycho's going to be doing all the driving and killing. As left-hand man, Fraquille won't even be used to wipe the captain's bum

The situation looks hopeless. But worse is to come. Much worse

As families gambolled around Miniland, or were underwhelmed by the Aero Nomad ride on that fateful day, did they even bother to consider what would happen if all those cheerful, six-foot-tall Lego figures of men and some women ever came to life? No, they probably didn't. Idiots.

(Note: Lego models are usually male, and the gender bias of Legoland's statue parks reflects this. Once again, it's a purist's pleasure. Would *Lego Got To Get Outta Here* be a good idea set in Dollyland? No. Obviously not. One Dolly Parton is scary and plastic enough. Sorry, Stephen Carmichael, but it's true.)

At first, neither the soldiers nor the terrorists register what's happening. They're too busy having gunfights on the Lego go-karts. Break neck stuff, as proved beyond doubt when a man has his neck broken by some falling hedge.

But then the fight's interrupted. Something comes crashing through what remains of the topiary. 'Slow the funk down, I ain't digging this groove,' all of them except the

Chinaman say. But the funk don't slow down. In fact, it speeds up. Into punk.

A nine-foot, living, breathing giraffe – *made of Lego* – stampedes into shot. It's followed by a pride of Lego lions, eight Lego chimps and the Lego station master from Lego City. Some Lego flamingos also turn up, but they don't really bother anyone.

With one great, savage arc of his baton, the Lego station master beheads the captain. Shaser is gutted. Sure, the captain put his balls in a vice, but he did it gently.

The terrorists and the soldiers turn their guns on the animals. But every time a Lego fiend is destroyed, its little blocks rebuild themselves into new and even more terrible shapes. The humans are forced into a truce: they must work together or die.

By this time, Shaser has worked out exactly what's happened. He explains that the terrorists' biological weapon has managed to fuse the Lego blocks into living organisms, because obviously nerve gas gives things new nerves. The logic of this being irrefutable, the nay sayers stop asking annoying questions.

Chaos reigns all around Legoland. Those unquestioning families – once so safe in their pathetic little bubbles – are being eaten by Lego dinosaurs, burnt to crisps by Lego dragons or hacked to death by Lego knights, mummies and Vikings. The closet psychopath is ripped apart by a million little ant-like Lego men.

The ranting super-terrorist 'makes like your mother and abandons'. (I love that saying. But – word of warning – use it sparingly in a school environment. You have no idea how sensitive some of the little buggers get about divorce. That said, his mother's sleeping arrangements bounce off Mitchell Harper's back like a duck off a car windscreen.)

Now the humans' undisputed leader, Shaser leads all the civilian survivors to shelter in Duplo Valley. (Duplo doesn't come alive.) Can Fraquille win back the trust and admiration of his fellow soldiers? Can he maintain an uneasy alliance with the terrorists while they fight the unholy plastic demons currently stamping all over Miniland? Will those Little Chef sausages come back to haunt Our Boys at just the wrong moment? The answer to all of those questions is, 'Yes, with differently messy consequences.'

If you wish to contribute some money to the production of Lego To Get Outta Here, please visit my JustGiving site. As a sop to the charity sector, I'm currently three weeks into my six-month pledge to stop waxing my body. Doesn't sound too bad? Let me tell you, when every inch of hair below your chin has been whipped off your body every week by a nimble Thai in his father's parlour, your follicles will take any opportunity to have their revenge. When naked, I currently look like a mid-70s Kevin Keegan from every conceivable angle. Trust me on that. God only knows what my body will be like in five months' time. SuBo's plughole springs to mind.

After-school Activities at Abbey Grove

The Austerity Years

From: Shaquille Fraser [mailto:SFraser@abbeygrove.co.uk]
Sent: 06 June 2013 12:59
To: Everyone
Subject: After-School Activities

Dear Gs and Hustlers,

Fraser here. Bad news first: the Tories are still in charge. The good news? I still have size five feet, which means I can rock wheelie shoes *and* the ones that flash. Silver lining, eh? That's the moral of this memo. To quote Alfie when his grandfather passed away: 'Yes, he's dead, but he had loads of cardigans. Kerching!'

OK, here goes. Unfortunately, the government's cut 100 per cent of our after-school activities cash. It turns out that they *really* need the money. I'll be honest, the whole 'economy in ruins' yawn kinda passed me by, but I have a direct quote from the local Tory MP:

> 'It was a very, very difficult choice, Mr. Fraser, between
> taxing bankers and robbing schoolchildren. Sadly, we've
> made our decision. So give us all of your f****** money.'

I don't want to cuss our Member of Parliament, but he really creeps me out. With his preppy glasses and baggy suits, he reminds me of an overgrown schoolboy, because I bet he's *always* bashing the bishop. When you've been a teacher this long, you recognize the type. That Zachary David lad in the third year, for instance, is always slouching around with a rosette of crunchy bog roll stuck to each heel.

Bastard. Our MP, not Zac. Zac's a good bloke, although his parents are a bit of a handful. And that reminds me – Isobel, the Davids are at my throat again, so *please* stop teaching pupils that the Jews killed Christ. Hard-line Catholicism isn't popular ATM, particularly when it's getting hard in kids' faces. And that's ATM as in 'at the moment', by the way, not the cash machine or, er, the other one.

Yes, so Michael Gove is a bastard. Sorry for the cussage. F-Bomb, calm down. Woah, Nelly! Actually, Nelly is a classic example of someone who found the silver lining. Yeah, his boy City Spud's doing a bid in the pen, eight-to-ten for a crime he didn't commit. But what did Nelly do? He stuck a plaster on his face as a shout-out to Spud and – boom! – a star is born. As I tell the kids, out of adversity comes 'Dilemma', 'Hot In Herre' and 'Pimp Juice'. And if that's not inspirational, I don't know what is.

Tings look bleak, though. The government has sold our footballs, tennis rackets and chessboards. They've even rented the music room out to a very nice family who are under the impression Abbey Grove is a luxury block of holiday flats, and that the caretaker is a kind of butler – Carson, if you like, albeit a Carson with Tourette's and a glass eye.

Some HR problems, meanwhile, have turned the financial downturn into a perfect storm. Our regular judo instructor has moved to Thailand with his mail-order bride. Sai-Pim's a lovely girl, and the judo teacher says that she's as close as he can get to his beloved Japan without needing to become conventionally attractive.

Mr Grotowski the drama teacher has alienated the kids with his intense rehearsals of a Polish-language *King Lear*. Even Stephen Carmichael isn't going back to drama club after Grotowski made them all writhe around in sackcloth and briar-thorn crowns, eating mud to commune with their inner peasant. Grotowski's hopeless. Last year, I told him to do *Grease*, and he gave us a twelve-hour version of Sophocles' tragedy *Oedipus*, performed in the original ancient Greek. That did not go down well with the Twihards.

Miss Julie the piano teacher, meanwhile, is still recovering from her massive nervous breakdown, though the doctors say she's doing well. Apparently, she's chimping the psychological evaluation panel with the apish gusto of a madwoman half her age. But it's a stark reminder to us all: the human mind can only stand so many bad renditions of 'Twinkle Twinkle Little Star'.

All in all, the chips are down in the gutter. But we have to take courage from Joe Poulter. He'd eat those chips, gutter or no gutter.

Chaps, it's up to us to come up with some cheap 'n' cheerful after-school activities. I've drawn up a list of suggestions, but I'd love your input, too. Remember, there's nothing we can't achieve if we work together. Plus, the PE teacher says I can borrow the gym if I destroy a laptop for him. Here's a list of my suggestions:

- **Cockfights**. Kids love animals, boys love violence, everyone loves chicken dippers. Plus, the kids could learn some Spanish/maths from the Mexican *chapitos* I've found to run the betting syndicate. *Arriba chiquitos!*

- **Ghost-Hunting**. Watch *Celebrity Ghost-Hunter* and you'll see just how cheap it is to chase the supernatural. All that show pays for is a darkened room, Paul Danan, and one runner slamming a door at random intervals. Even if they paid for Danan's taxi back to panto, it can't cost more than £200 an episode. Obviously we'd have to raise our game a bit. I know it sometimes seems like Abbey Grove is little more than a kennels, but Danan, Lee from Blue, James 'Arg' Argent and The Saturdays have far lower mental capacities than even our thickest class, 2J. God, that class makes me €}:-O (the Euro in that terrified smiley is the bald head of Mr Parling, 2J's English teacher, may he rest in peace). Basically, it'll take more than a slamming door to convince our pupils that ghosts exist. So I thought we could put Mrs Westurby in a white sheet then hide her insulin. That roving, groaning apparition would scare me shizless! And the whole thing would only cost the price of a Twix, just in case Westurby doesn't sniff out her medicine in time.

- **Tantric Yoga**. Miss G's suggested this one, and I'm mad fer it. I love to get my chakras stiff. The only thing is, Rosie, some of the parents have complained about your, er, *frankness* vis-à-vis sex. We're all in favour of the kids playing safe, but I'm not sure they need to know positions like 'The Reverse Gardener', 'Krishna's Brick-Hod' and 'The Cheeky Butler's Treat'. Don't get me wrong, I want this school to churn out grade A shaggers.

But look at it from a parent's perspective: you can play all the whale-song and Tibetan chanting you like, you're still teaching them the Karma Sutra.

• **Boxing**. This can't be too hard, right? It's just four gloves and two toothless old men to sponge buckets of bloody water over the kids in between rounds. Also, if I stop straightening my hair, I go from Brian Ferry to Don King in about a week. Throw in some of Alfie's granddad's old suits and we've got eccentric press conferences covered!

• **Imagination Land**. What could be more wonderful than the imagination of a child? It's like every kid has *Mr Benn* in their head – another day, another adventure in a magical world. The imagination can turn even a no-hoper like Reggie Blinker into an astronaut, a knight in shining armour or a Frenchwoman. It truly is the most precious gift, and one we should never exploit or cheapen. Hence Imagination Land, i.e. a classroom/store-cupboard where we lock the kids for an hour and tell them to have fun in their heads. In silence. We can get the caretaker to supervise, because his time is worth less than ours, and his terrifying manner tends to keep the children in line.

• **Cleaning**. Don't be sniffy – it's a life skill. I know I can say, hand on heart, that my life was changed by seeing the care and ingenuity the caretaker puts into clearing up a puddle of vomit. And, just as sawdust soaked up Philippa Stamp's little accident, why not let the kids soak up the caretaker's wealth of knowledge? Which is not to say that he's sick. He's a man of exotic tastes, perhaps, but not sick.

Over and out,

Fray Man Scoop

Boulevardier, anecdotalist, G: married to the street

From: Rosie Gulliver [mailto:RGulliver@abbeygrove.co.uk]
Sent: 06 June 2013 17:58
To: Everyone
Subject: After-School Activities

Hi everyone,

I agree with Fraser. These cuts make me so angry, but I want to use that anger productively. I thought we could get the kids involved in their own community a bit more. Maybe we could take them to help at old people's homes or hospices? The elderly could teach our pupils about the Second World War, which may be no bad thing, because Alfie's lessons on WWII are little more than the first twenty minutes of *Saving Private Ryan* on loop.

Actually, that's not fair. Remember Alfie's friend, Atticus Hoye? The one who touched Alf's bottom at the Eden Centre? Well, Atticus put Alfie in touch with a German history teacher about Alfie's age. Atticus, it seems, had met this German, Herr Schweinliber, in some kind of nightclub. Alfie wasn't clear on what kind of club it was, but it sounds like it didn't have any urinals. Anyway, Atticus and Schweinliber helped each other to relieve themselves, one thing led to another, and now Alfie and this German are getting their respective classes to play Call of Duty: World of War online against each other. The German pupils play as Nazis, our kids as the Allies, and they shout insults at each other down headsets. This, apparently, is what qualifies as interactive learning.

If the elderly don't appeal, Abbey Grove pupils could play with children who have mental or physical handicaps, or they could go on an environmental drive (recycling, cleaning rivers etc)? I myself volunteer one night a week at a soup kitchen. We serve food to the homeless and dispossessed; numbers are growing every day thanks to the government's austerity measures. I would love to take along some Abbey Grove pupils the next time I go – it's such a fun, humbling, positive thing to do.

Alfie, maybe you could research activities with a historical slant? I don't want to sound like a nag, but we need to win some brownie points from Ofsted after those GCSEs results. To quote Fraser, your pupils got 'more Es than a Happy Mondays gig'. Anything we can do to show them we're changing our ways, the better.

Yours,
Rosie

P.S. Alfie, please could you change whatever it is you did to the bottom of my emails? I don't know what it is but it comes up automatically and it's really, really embarrassing.

The fit one

From: Alfie Wickers [mailto:AWickers@abbeygrove.co.uk]
Sent: 06 June 2013 18:01
To: Everyone
Subject: After-School Activities

Yo,

Sorry I haven't replied to this for so long. Fraser's emails go straight to my junk mail ever since I started getting those ones sent from his account with the subject heading: WOULD U LIKE A BIGGER P*NIS? It turns out his account hadn't been hacked – Fraser was genuinely curious about whether the male members of staff were happy with their bodies (Fraser's asked me to point that out, like it makes him sound any less weird). And for the record, show me a man who says he doesn't need a bigger penis, and I'll show you a liar or Channing Tatum. Seriously, next time you watch *Dear John*, freeze-frame any scene on the beach and boom. It's there all right. It made me feel a bit inadequate, but Atticus was freeze-framing all night.

Anyway, can everyone get off my back over those stupid exams? I don't think the GCSEs are a fair reflection of my teaching methods. I'm a teacher, not a robot. Oh sorry, Ofsted, my pupils have 'personalities' rather than 'qualifications'. But what do you think is gonna get them further in the real world? Academic grades or a thorough knowledge of all the goofs in *Gladiator*? What's more useful, an A* or the ability to spot an extra wearing a digital wristwatch? What will make Britain prouder: a load of pen-pushing pussies or a unit of toughened *C.O.D.* marines who can frag Germans in their sleep? I rest my case.

Having said that, Rosie, I do take Ofsted's point. So I've done some research into historical games. Most of them sound really cool, if potentially lethal. Swings and roundabouts, then, but that's better than tramps and pensioners. Listening to a ninety-year-old women remembering their boyish soldier husbands getting killed in the Ardennes is just depressing, and who wants to dole out Baxters to some beardy flasher? Sorry, Rosie, but it's true. I get the theory, but making Mitchell play with some handicapped kids – I mean, haven't they suffered enough?

These games are all taken from a Tudor-times rule book that I dug up in the Tring archives. The most completely mad game in it, by the way, is called 'Mole or Shrew'. The book says: 'Thys is not for the fayre-of-hearted diceman or wench,' mainly because the aim of 'Mole or Shrew' is to leave its players either blind or frigid. So there's no way we're playing that – Pickwell would win the frigid thing hands down; even the Arctic explorer Sir Ranulph Fiennes couldn't survive in her for long.

Here are some of the more practical sports I found.

HISTORICAL SPORT NO. 1 is **Cotswarber**. It originated in the enlightened court of short-lived monarch Ethelred the Queer (834–835). Medieval people must have had a lot of time on their hands, cos the game takes three hours to set up. Perhaps that's why Alfred the Great invented clocks, just to speed shit up a bit. (It's beyond me how my pupils can get bad grades when I'm cracking history gags of that quality.)

Cotswarber has two five-a-side teams. The King's Men play in red hats, the Barons in blue hats. They start at either end of a rectangular pitch, at the centre of which is a platform. On this platform is 'the baby's cot'. The teams are arranged in a four-man diamond formation, with the fifth player or 'babbypoach' in the centre. All the players wear wings made out of feathers and wax, and beaks of lead for striking their opposite numbers. The aim of the game is to steal the 'baby' from out of the cot, which is securely fastened to the back of a dog. This dog has been driven completely mad by the third official, who traditionally taunts the animal with hot bitches for a couple of weeks before the game.

So far, so straightforward. But the old book says that 'these playars moste have to runne in the direction their wings tak themme – and their wings have a minde of their own!' This 'minde' is made up of a hundred wasps per man on the King's side, and three hundred moths per Baron. The insects have to be hand-tied to the wings with 'sturdy stringes'. The historical source notes that 'this can be bothe laborious and peinfull'.

The theory is the wasps and moths are both drawn to the 'baby', which is actually a pig's liver coated in honey with some lit candles stuck in it. (I suggest that, if we do play Cotswarber, instead of the insects, we just get the teams drunk on different drinks, i.e. the mothy ones we get pissed on real ale, the wasp ones on vodka. Dunno if this is appropriate, but I'm spitballing.)

Games of Cotswarber end only when one of the babbypoaches has wrestled the baby from the cot or the rival team and eaten it, or when the mad dog has succeeded in tearing off the cot and having sex with either its own 'child' or one of the players.

Yeah, it's pretty trippy. The health and safety brigade would have a prolapse at the wasps/rabid dog element, but Eton still plays Cotswarber, and no one's died since 2005. Strange how these insane, elitist, out-of-date traditions still thrive at public schools.

HISTORICAL SPORT NO. 2 is **Goose-stepping**. Famously, Goose-stepping was Enid the Unyielding's favourite pastime. This is largely because the geese didn't ask him why he had a woman's name, unlike everyone else.

In Enid's day (approx. 960–983), the referee would fill a pen on the village green with geese. Competitors took turns to leap from goose to goose – imagine a kind of long jump with sound effects. The rules state that, when the player successfully lands on a bird, he must shout 'Gobble-gobble, God Save the King' – even if it's a queen at the time. This is 'one of Enid's subtille revenges uppon the monarches of the future'. The Goose-stepping winner traditionally wore a necklace of geese-heads, and stuffed their wives with feathers.

The only issue with Goose-stepping is the cost of buying all those geese. Though the dead could easily feed a class or two. And I imagine goose tastes better than the horsemeat we're used to eating.

HISTORICAL SPORT NO. 3 is called **Hopsychair**. This is the least feasible of the three. Basically, Hopsychair is a bit like musical chairs, only instead of running around the chairs you have to hop from them in a prescribed way. 'The knees muste bende, the back be straite – the best playars don't putte on weight,' the merry Hopsychair players of yesteryear used to sing. The real problem, though, is that, instead of playing it in a living room or church hall, Hopsychair takes place on a rickety platform over the sea. And the chairs are on fire. Also, the music must be provided by a hurdy-gurdy played by a man with one eye. I'm not sure why.

Hopsychair's biggest controversy happened in about AD1034, when the English captain, Yod Littleterry, abused a teammate's brother for coming from Kent and not Essex (allegedly calling him a 'f****** Kentish c***'). Although everyone knew exactly what Littleterry said, the barons refused to do anything about it. The only consequence was a brief bout of refusing to shake hands, and the death of any remaining respect felt for the squalid, thoroughly mediocre Hopsychair national team.

Today, the whole story's quite hard to understand. I guess that's because we've evolved – we don't abuse others on the basis of where they come from, so to get into the mind of a disgusting Neanderthal like Yod Littleterry is nigh-on impossible.

Is that enough history now? I'm kind of sick of it.

Alfie

Lash-master general

From: Isobel Pickwell [mailto:IPickwell@abbeygrove.co.uk]
Sent: 06 June 2013 20:18
To: Everyone
Subject: After-School Activities

Jesus wept.

Shall I tell you what the pupils at St. Jennifer's School For Girls did 'for fun'? Do you want to know what 'after-school clubs' were on offer to the virgins of East Kilbride? Prayer. Penance. Unpicking knotted hemp rope. Stolen, angry kisses over the Laundromat. More penance. Returning to the Laundromat to sit on it, knickerless, as it reached its final, earth-shattering cycle. Yet more penance. More rope. Knot-tying, around a doughty beam. Toying with the noose. Unpicking the noose. More penance. Thinking of your father, the butcher; come Saturday, you'd be back working in his shop, weighing livers and smoking the flanks of swine. Sleep. Restless sleep.

All that made me the woman I am today. And I defy you to tell me why these mollycoddled little rodents deserve any better.

Do not contact me again. Especially you, Fraser. Why would I want a bigger penis, given that I come into contact with you every day?

IP

P.S. And Wickers, though I hate to sound like Little Miss Gulliver, sort out whatever it is you've done to my e-message or I'll gut you like a veal calf. I can't make you respect my beliefs, but I will not sit idly by as you use His name in vain.

Führer

ABBEY GROVE SCHOOL

Thus concludes my evidence against Abbey Grove, its teaching staff and certain strains of the student body. I'm sure you'll agree that <u>something must be done</u>. And I must warn you that, if you are unwilling to act, then I am perfectly happy to go it alone. The time for words is at an end. I have a crossbow. You have been warned.

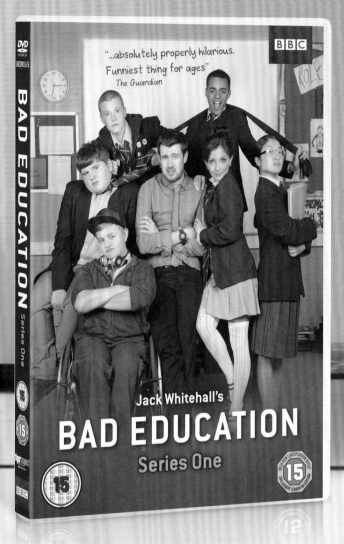